POCKET

SHANTYMAN

130 Songs of the Sea

Music & Lyrics
Compiled by Gary Coover

ROLLSTON PRESS

The Pocket Shantyman
by Gary Coover

ISBN-13: 978-0-9970748-3-3
ISBN-10: 0-9970748-3-3

Other books by Gary Coover:

Anglo Concertina in the Harmonic Style
Christmas Concertina
Civil War Concertina
Easy Anglo 1-2-3
75 Irish Session Tunes for Anglo Concertina

ROLLSTON PRESS
330 N. Rollston Avenue
Fayetteville, AR 72701
USA

TABLE OF CONTENTS

INTRODUCTION

Ahoy, there – sailors, folksingers, pirates and gamers! Here are over a hundred sea songs and sea shanties that I've enjoyed singing and listening to for many many years. Some are work songs, others are for the slack times between the work, but all are songs of the sea.

This is not a work of scholarship – it is a book for singers. It is a personal treasury of favorites learned from a wide variety of sources both recorded and live and credited where remembered. With few exceptions, all of the words and tunes are traditional, anonymous, or of unknown or forgotten provenance.

Shanties often go by many different names, may have very different words and sometimes the tunes are completely different too. All part of the folk process – hopefully you can find many of your favorites here.

The songs are shown with melodies in standard musical notation. Of course, you'll need to adjust the pitch to suit your own singing, but if nothing else the relative positions of the notes will help guide you along.

These songs have been tested on board ship as well as on stage, and may or may not vary from what you might be familiar with. That's ok – just adjust and adapt as sailors and singers would have done in the olden days.

With this handy little book in your pocket you'll have an oceanful of tunes ever at the ready to enjoy, educate, entertain, or perhaps put into service to help raise a halyard, man a pump or turn a capstan. Or to lift some spirits or hoist a pint or two instead. Always ready, in your pocket, so you can be the shantyman.

May you always sing loud, strong and steady, with plenty of wind in your sails, grog in your belly and joy and adventure in your heart.

THE SEA SHANTY

Sea shanties were originally work songs utilized to help organize the actions and lessen the boredom of long, difficult, repetitive chores on large sailing ships at sea.

Often categorized by the type of work they are best suited for, there can be long-drag or short drag shanties, halyard shanties, windlass shanties, capstan shanties, pumping shanties, cargo stowing shanties, etc.

Sea songs and shanties historically come in a wide variety of shapes and sizes, with lyrics and melodies often varying greatly between different versions. Improvisation was the order of the day, with bits and pieces often borrowed from other songs or made up on the spot – there is no such thing as only one true correct version of any of these songs.

Shanties are also often known by a variety of names, depending on who learned it where, and from whom, and what name they chose to remember it by. If you don't see one of your favorites in the book just try looking for it under several alternate names.

Other sea songs, known as forebitters, were for periods of downtime, for helping pass the time during long voyages at sea. Or perhaps for enjoying with a few pints in the pub once back on shore.

Verses and choruses often reflect sailors' hopes and fears, with many a commentary on working conditions, food, crew, thoughts of home or the girls on shore.

The heyday of the shanty was the mid 19th century on the great tallships of the merchant marine. The advent of steam and diesel power greatly changed the working conditions at sea. Shanties are still used aboard some sailing ships, but most are now sung for entertainment, for historical reenactments and are even found on video games like "Assassin's Creed".

THE SHANTYMAN

The role of the shantyman was not just for musical amusement during the long voyage, although many songs were sung to pass the time away.

Coordinating tedious hard work by numerous hands requires a steady beat to ensure everyone heaves or pulls together in unison, and it was the job of the shantyman to provide the rhythm and the beat that got the work done in the most efficient and effective way possible.

It was the shantyman who selected the right song and right number of verses to maintain the proper pace until the task was complete

He would also often be called upon to provide light entertainment during the long breaks between work. For these songs he might even break out a fiddle or a concertina for accompaniment.

Along with officers like the captain, first mate, bosun and navigator, the shantyman was a crucially important member of a sailing ship's crew since he provided the cadences that got the work done while also helping keep the crew amused and entertained during the long voyages at sea.

A HUNDRED YEARS AGO

1. A hundred years on the eastern shore
   OH YES OH
   A hundred years on the eastern shore
   A HUNDRED YEARS AGO

2. Oh when I sailed across the sea
   My gal said she'd be true to me

3. I promised her a golden ring
   She promised me that little thing

4. Oh up aloft this yard must go
   For mister mate has told us so

5. I thought I heard the old man say
   That we was homeward bound today

A TALL SHIP FOR TEXAS

(Tom Goux)

1. She's an old iron bark
    But a lady quite fine
    A century working the seas
    And her masts and her spars
    Once more they will shine
    She'll run once again with the breeze

    AND SHE'LL SAIL AGAIN BOYS
    SHE'LL SAIL ONCE MORE
    SHE'LL DANCE O'ER THE OCEAN
    AS SHE'S DONE BEFORE
    BY GALVESTON'S STRAND
    YOU'LL FIND HER MADE FAST
    SHE'S A TALL SHIP FOR TEXAS – ELISSA

2. From Cardiff to Brazil
   She hauled the black coal
   Returning with sugar and wheat
   Or cotton, mahogany
   Resin or oil
   All cargo delivered one hundred years toil

3. In Rangoon and Boston
   Her masthead was seen
   All seven seas were her realm
   Her owners were portly
   Her sailors were lean
   Her masters were skilled at the helm

4. So lift up a glass
   To this fine lofty ship
   Returned and revived from the smuggler's grip
   And here's to those souls
   Who have saved her from hell
   Your work's all but done and you've done it right well

5. Elissa refitted
   Stand ready to meet
   The twenty-first century breeze
   And our children's children
   Will haul on her sheets
   They'll have a tall ship for their seas

From the singing of Tom Goux & Jacek Sulanowski
Live aboard "Elissa", Galveston, Texas

A WIFE IN EVERY PORT

1. I'm sailin' away in the morning
   I'm sailin' away on the tide
   And when I return again
   Lassie will ye be my bride
   WILL YE BE MY BRIDE, ME BOYS
   WILL YE BE MY BRIDE
   AND WHEN I RETURN AGAIN
   LASSIE WILL YE BE MY BRIDE

2. Laddie I will wait for you
   As long as me life
   Laddie I will wait for you
   And I'll be a sailor's wife
   I'LL BE A SAILOR'S WIFE, ME BOYS
   I'LL BE A SAILOR'S WIFE
   LADDIE I WILL WAIT FOR YOU
   AND I'LL BE A SAILOR'S WIFE

3. Oh the sun it shone and the wind it blew
    And the ship sailed out to sea
    When she caught the eye of a soldier lad
    Who was standing on the quay
    STANDING ON THE QUAY, ME BOYS
    STANDING ON THE QUAY
    SHE CAUGHT THE EYE OF A SOLDIER LAD
    WHO WAS STANDING ON THE QUAY

4. And the storm it raged and the cannons roared
    And driving was the rain
    After twelve months at the sea
    He was homeward bound again
    HOMEWARD BOUND AGAIN, ME BOYS
    HOMEWARD BOUND AGAIN
    AFTER TWELVE MONTHS AT THE SEA
    HE WAS HOMEWARD BOUND AGAIN

5. And there he met her at the docks
    With a baby in her arms
    Saying I'm sorry my sailor lad
    But I fell for a soldier's charms
    I FELL FOR A SOLDIER'S CHARMS, ME BOYS
    I FELL FOR A SOLDIER'S CHARMS
    SAYING I'M SORRY MY SAILOR LAD
    BUT I FELL FOR A SOLDIER'S CHARMS

6. Don't you worry me bonnie lass
    Was the sailor's bold retort
    Don't you worry me bonnie lass
    I've a wife in every port
    A WIFE IN EVERY PORT, ME BOYS
    A WIFE IN EVERY PORT
    DON'T YOU WORRY, ME BONNIE LASS
    I'VE A WIFE IN EVERY PORT

From the singing of Ian Benzie (Old Blind Dogs)

A-ROVING

1. In Amsterdam there lived a maid
   MARK WELL WHAT I DO SAY
   In Amsterdam there lived a maid
   And she was mistress of her trade
   WE'LL GO NO MORE A-ROVING WITH YOU FAIR MAID

   A-ROVING, A-ROVING, SINCE ROVING'S BEEN MY RUIN
   WE'LL GO NO MORE A-ROVING WITH YOU FAIR MAID

2. One night I crept from my abode
   To meet this fair maid down the road

3. I met this fair maid after dark
   And took her to her favorite park

4. I took this fair maid for a walk
   And we had such loving talk

5. I put my arm around her waist
   Said she young man you're in great haste

6. I put my hand upon her knee
   Said she young man you're rather free

7. I put my hand upon her thigh
   Said she young man you're rather high

8. I put my hand upon her lap
   She said young man you'll catch the clap

ADIEU SWEET LOVELY NANCY

1. Adieu sweet lovely Nancy
   Ten thousand times adieu
   I'm a-going across the ocean love
   To seek for something new
   Come change your ring with me dear girl
   Come change your ring with me
   For it might be a token of true love
   While I am on the sea

2. And when I'm far upon the sea
   You know not where I am
   Kind letters I will write to you
   From every foreign land
   The secrets of your heart dear girl
   Are the best of my good will
   So let your body be where it might
   My heart will be with you still

3. There's a heavy storm arising
   See how it gathers 'round
   While we poor souls on the ocean wide
   Are fighting for the crown
   There's nothing to protect us love
   Or keep us from the cold
   On the ocean wide where we must fight
   Like jolly seamen bold

4. There's tinkers, tailors, shoemakers
   Lie snoring fast asleep
   While we poor souls on the ocean wide
   Are a-ploughing through the deep
   Our officers commanded us
   And then we must obey
   Expecting every moment
   For to get cast away

5. But when the wars are over
   There'll be peace on every shore
   We'll return to our wives and our families
   And the girls that we adore
   We'll call for liquor merrily
   And spend our money free
   And when the money is all gone
   We'll boldly go to sea

From the singing of the Copper Family, and
Tim Hart and Maddy Prior

ADIEU YOU PRETTY NANCY

(Chris Sugden)

1. Now the Queen she wants seamen
   To sail on the sea
   Which made pretty William
   To cry and to grieve
   Saying Polly dearest Polly
   Let me stay behind
   For my pretty little bottom
   Will freeze in the wind
   MY PRETTY LITTLE BOTTOM
   WILL FREEZE IN THE WIND

2. Now Polly dearest Polly
   Was a stout-hearted lass
   She say pretty William
   Don't you be such an ass
   You'll make me look foolish
   If you stay on shore
   While the other bold Williams
   Are a-going to war
   WHILE THE OTHER…

3. Well William's afraid
   That the ship will be sunk
   But the Queen still wants seamen
   And men who've got spunk
   So William's gone on board
   For a sailor to go
   And the sailor went for William
   And he took him below
   AND THE SAILOR...

4. Well they had not been a-sailing
   Past three days or four
   When the Captain says
   Haven't I seen you before
   Aren't you a young maiden
   Dressed up as a man
   And William say Captain
   Prove that if you can
   AND WILLIAM SAY...

5. Well he stripped him stark naked
   And he took of his clothes
   And he had to admit
   You're a man I suppose
   He stripped him he whipped him
   Before all the men
   And the men said
   It's our turn now do it again
   AND THE MEN SAID...

6. Well the war is now ended
   And the fighting is o'er
   So William returned
   To his Polly on the shore
   He hugged her he kissed her
   He swore he'll be true
   But she say hold hard
   I don't recognize you
   BUT SHE SAY…

7. His hand in his pocket
   Pretty William has put
   And he drew out two sovereigns
   And an old rabbit's foot
   And a long piece of string
   And a penknife that's broken
   But the one thing he can't find
   Is a true lover's token
   BUT THE ONE THING…

8. So adieu you pretty nancy boy
   You're not welcome here
   And William again
   For the docks he do steer
   I'll go to sea once more
   On one of them there whalers
   I won't fool with girls
   I'll stick to rum and sailors
   I WON'T FOOL WITH…

From the singing of Sid and Henry Kipper

ALABAMA JOHN CHEROKEE

1. John Cherokee was an Indian man
   ALABAMA JOHN CHEROKEE
   He run away every time he can
   ALABAMA JOHN CHEROKEE

   AWAY, HEY-O
   ALABAMA JOHN CHEROKEE
   AWAY, HEY-O
   ALABAMA JOHN CHEROKEE

2. They put him aboard a Yankee ship
   Again he gave the boss the slip

3. They catch him again and chain him tight
   And starve him many a day and night

4. Nothin' to drink and nothin' to eat
   He just fall dead at the boss's feet

5. So they bury him by the old gate post
   The very same day you can see his ghost

From the singing of Caryl P. Weiss

ALL FOR ME GROG

ALL FOR ME GROG, ME JOLLY JOLLY GROG
ALL FOR ME BEER AND TOBACCO
FOR I SPENT ALL ME TIN
ON THE LASSES DRINKING GIN
AND ACROSS THE WESTERN OCEAN I MUST WANDER

1. Where is me boots, me noggin noggin boots
    ALL GONE FOR BEER AND TOBACCO
    For the leather's all worn out
    And the heels are knocked about
    And me toes are looking out for better weather

2. Where is me shirt, me noggin noggin shirt
    For the color is wore out
    And the front is knocked about
    And the tail is looking out for better weather

3. Where is my wench, me noggin noggin wench
    Oh her lips is all wore out
    And her front is knocked about
    Now her tail is looking out for better weather

4. And where is me bed, me noggin noggin bed
    For the mattress is all tore
    For I lent it to a whore
    Now the springs are looking out for better weather

*From the singing of Jeff Warner, Gerret Warner, Louis Killen
and John "Fud" Benson*

BANKS OF GREEN WILLOW

1. Oh it's of a sea-captain
   Down by the banks of willow
   He's courted a pretty girl
   'Til she proved with child-o

2. She cried what shall I do my love
   What will become of me
   My mother and father
   They both will disown me

3. Go fetch me some of your father's gold
   And some of your mother's money
   And you shall sail the ocean
   Along with young Johnny

4. So she's fetched him some of her father's gold
   And some of her mother's money
   And she has gone aboard a ship
   Along with young Johnny

5. Well they had not been sailing
   Scarce six weeks nor so many
   Before she was delivered
   Of a beautiful baby

6. Sea captain, sea captain
    Here's fifty pounds for thee
    To see me safe home again
    Me and my baby

7. Oh no said the captain
    Such things they never can be
    'Tis better to lose two lives
    Than 'tis to lose many

8. Then tie the napkin round my head
    Come tie it soft and easy
    And throw me right overboard
    Me and my baby

9. So they tied the napkin round her head
    They've tied it soft and easy
    They've thrown her right overboard
    She and her baby

10. Don't you see how she swims, my lad
    Don't you see how her body quivers
    She'll swim 'til she comes to
    The banks of green willow

11. And my love shall have a coffin made
    Of a gold that shines yellow
    And she shall be buried
    On the banks of green willow

From the singing of Tony Rose

BANKS OF NEWFOUNDLAND

You bul - ly boys of Li - ver-pool I'll have you all be - ware.
When you sail in the pack - et ships no dun-gar-ree jum - pers wear. But
have a big mon - key jack - et all rea - dy to your hand. For there
blows some cold nor' - west - ers on the banks of New-found - land. WE'LL
SCRAPE HER AND WE'LL SCRUB HER WITH HO - LY STONE AND SAND, AND WE'LL
THINK OF THEM COLD NOR' - WEST - ERS ON THE BANKS OF NEW-FOUND - LAND.

1. You bully boys of Liverpool
   I'd have you to beware
   When you sail in the packet ships
   No dungaree jumpers wear
   But have a big monkey jacket
   All ready to your hand
   For there blows some cold nor'westers
   Off the banks of Newfoundland

   WE'LL SCRAPE HER AND WE'LL SCRUB HER
   WITH HOLY STONE AND SAND
   AND WE'LL THINK OF THEM COLD NOR'WESTERS
   ON THE BANKS OF NEWFOUNDLAND

2. There was Jack Lynch from Ballynahinch
    Mike Murphy and some more
    I tell you well they suffered like hell
    On the way to Baltimore
    They pawned their gear in Liverpool
    And they sailed as they did stand
    And there blows some cold nor'westers
    On the banks of Newfoundland

3. The mate he stood on the fo'c'sle head
    And loudly he did roar
    Now rattle her in me lucky lads
    We're bound for America's shore
    Go wash the mud off that dead man's face
    And heave to beat the band
    For there blows some cold nor'westers
    On the banks of Newfoundland

4. So now it's reef and reef me boys
    With the canvas frozen hard
    And it's mount and pass every mother's son
    On a ninety-foot tops'l yard
    Never mind about boots and oilskins
    But haul or you'll be damned
    For there blows some cold nor'westers
    On the banks of Newfoundland

5. And now we're off the hook me boys
    And the land's all white with snow
    But soon we'll see the pay table
    And have all night below
    And on the docks, come down in flocks
    Them pretty girls will stand
    Sayin' it's snugger with me than it is at sea
    On the banks of Newfoundland

From the singing of Ewan MacColl and A.L. Lloyd

BARRACK STREET

1. You sailors all come lend an ear
   Come listen to my song
   A trick of late was played on me
   And it won't detain you long
   I come from sea the other day
   And a girl I chanced to meet
   Oh me friends will be expecting me
   To a dance in Barrack Street

2. I said my young fair maid
   I cannot dance so well
   Besides I am to Windsor bound
   Where all my friends do dwell
   Been to sea the past two years
   I've saved up thirty pounds
   My friends will be expecting me
   This night in Windsor town

3. Well if you cannot dance me love
   Then you shall stand a treat
   Have a glass or two of brandy
   And a something for to eat
   At six o'clock this evening
   I'll meet you off the train
   So don't forget to give a call
   When you come to town again

4. At eight o'clock that evening
    Then the drinking did begin
    And when we all had drunk our fill
    The dancing did begin
    Me and my love danced all around
    To a merry tune
    She says my dear let us retire
    To a chamber alone

5. So dancing being over
    And to bed we did repair
    And there I fell fast asleep
    The truth I will declare
    My darling with me thirty pounds
    Gold watch and chain had fled
    Left me here poor Jack alone
    Stark naked in bed

6. So I looked all around me
    And there's nothing I could spy
    But a woman's shirt and apron
    All on the bed did lie
    I wrung my hands and tore my hair
    Crying oh what shall I do
    Fare thee well sweet Windsor town
    I'm sure I'll never see you

7. Well everything being silent
    And the hour but twelve o'clock
    I put on the shirt and apron
    And I steered for Crowman's Wharf
    The captain says now Jack I thought
    You were to Windsor bound
    You might have got a better suit
    Than that for thirty pound

8. I might have got a better suit
   If I'd had got the chance
   I met a girl in Barrack Street
   She took me to a dance
   I danced me own destruction
   Now I'm struck from head to feet
   I swear that I won't go no more
   Down in Barrack Street

9. So all of you young sailor lads
   A warning take from me
   Beware of all your company
   When you go out on a spree
   And keep clear of Barrack Street
   Or else you'll rue the day
   In a woman's shirt and apron
   Oh they'll bring you out to sea

From the singing of Nic Jones

THE BLACK BALL LINE

1. I served me time in the Black Ball Line
   TO ME WAY HEY HEY HOO RIO
   On the Black Ball Line I served me time
   HOORAH FOR THE BLACK BALL LINE

2. Oh the Black Ball Line is good and true
   The Black Ball Line's for me and you

3. There was once a Black Ball Ship
   That 14 knots an hour could clip

4. Oh take a trip to Liverpool
   Liverpool that Yankee School

5. Oh Yankee sailors you all see there
   Red top boots and short back hair

6. Oh eighteen knots with the wind abaft
   Stand by your halyards fore and aft

7. Oh drink a health to the Black Ball Line
   Their ships are stout and their men are fine

From the singing of David Marston, Charles O'Hegarty and David Jones (The Starboard List)

BLOW THE MAN DOWN

1. Well as I was a-walkin' down Paradise Street
   TO ME WAY HEY BLOW THE MAN DOWN
   A charming young damsel I chanced for to meet
   GIVE ME SOME TIME TO BLOW THE MAN DOWN

2. She was round in the counter and bluff in the bow
   I threw out my hawser I took her in tow

3. Oh she said to me sir will you stand the treat
   Delighted says I for a damsel so sweet

4. It was up in her quarters she piped me aboard
   And there on her bed I cut loose with my sword

5. But just as my cutter was forging ahead
   She shouted my husband and jumped out of bed

6. He was seven feet tall he had a chest like a horse
   And right for my jawbone he plotted his course

7. He loosened my rigging he kicked in my stays
   I flew down the stairs like a ship on the waves

8. I chanced on a packet that happened on by
   And when I awoke I was bound for Shanghai

9. So come all you young laddies who'd follow the sea
   Don't never take heed of what fair damsels say

From the singing of Louis Killen, Jeff Warner, Gerret Warner,
and Fud Benson

BLOW YE WINDS

1. 'Tis advertised in Boston
   New York and Buffalo
   A hundred hearty sailors
   A-whalin' for to go

   SINGIN' BLOW YE WINDS IN THE MORNIN'
   BLOW YE WINDS HI HO
   HAUL AWAY YOUR RUNNIN' GEAR AND
   BLOW, BOYS, BLOW

2. They tell you of the clipper ships
   A-runnin' in and out
   They say you'll take five hundred sperm
   Before you're six months out

3. They send you to New Bedford town
   A famous whaling port
   They give you to some land sharks
   Who board and fit you out

4. And now we're out to sea my boys
   The wind comes on to blow
   With half the watch sick on deck
   The other half below

5. The captain's on the after deck
   A-squintin' at the sails
   When up above the lookout spots
   A mighty school of whales

6. It's lower down the boats, my boys
   And after him we'll travel
   But if you get too near his fluke
   He'll kick you to the devil

7. And now that he is ours, my boys
   We'll bring him alongside
   Then over with our blubber hooks
   And rob him of his hide

8. When we get home, our ship made fast
   And we get through our sailin'
   A brimmin' glass around we'll pass
   And damn this blubber whalin'

From the singing of Michael Cooney

BOLD BENJAMIN-O

1. Brave Admiral Cole he's gone to sea
   Oh me boys-O
   Brave Admiral Cole he's gone to sea-O
   Brave Admiral Cole has gone to sea
   All along of his ship's company
   On board the bold Benjamin-O

2. We sailed our course away for Spain
   Oh my boys-O
   We sailed our course away for Spain-O
   We sailed our course away for Spain
   Our silver and gold for to gain
   On board the bold Benjamin-O

3. We sailed out five hundred men
   Oh me boys-O
   We sailed out five hundred men-O
   We sailed out five hundred men
   And brought back but sixty one
   They was lost in bold Benjamin-O

4. And when we came to Blackwall
   Oh my boys-O
   When we came to Blackwall-O
   And when we came to Blackwall
   Our captain so loud did call
   Here comes the bold Benjamin-O

5. Here's the mothers a-crying for their sons
   Oh me boys-O
   Here's the mothers a-crying for their sons-O
   Here's the mothers a-crying for their sons
   And the widows for their husbands
   That was lost in bold Benjamin-O

From the singing of Peter Bellamy, Royston Wood and Heather Wood

BOLD RILEY

Oh — the rain it rains all the day long. ____

BOLD RI - LEY, OH — BOLD RI - LEY. ____

And — the nor - thern wind it blows so strong. ____

BOLD RI - LEY - O'S ____ GONE A - WAY.

GOOD - BYE MY SWEET - HEART, GOOD - BYE MY DEAR - O. ____

BOLD - RI - LEY - O, ____ BOLD RI - LEY.

GOOD - BYE MY DAR - LING, ____ GOOD - BYE MY DEAR - O. ____

BOLD RI - LEY - O'S ____ GONE A - WAY.

1. Oh the rain it rains all the day long
    BOLD RILEY-O, BOLD RILEY
    And the northern wind it blows so strong
    BOLD RILEY-O'S GONE AWAY

    GOODBYE MY SWEETHEART, GOODBYE MY DEAR-O
    BOLD RILEY-O, BOLD RILEY
    GOODBYE MY DARLING, GOODBYE MY DEAR-O
    BOLD RILEY-O'S GONE AWAY

2. Our anchor is weighed and our rags are well set
    And those Liverpool girls we will never forget

3. We're outward bound for the Bengal Bay
    Get bending me lads it's a hell of a way
    From the singing of John Jones and The Oyster Band

THE BONNIE SHIP THE DIAMOND

1. Oh the Diamond is a ship me lads
   For the Davis Strait she's bound
   And the quay it is all garnished
   With bonnie lasses 'round
   Captain Thompson gives the order
   To sail the ocean wide
   Where the sun it never sets me lads
   Nor darkness dims the tide

   AND IT'S CHEER UP ME LADS
   LET YOUR HEARTS NEVER FAIL
   WHILE THE BONNIE SHIP THE DIAMOND
   GOES A-FISHING FOR THE WHALE

2. Here's a health to the Resolution
   Likewise the Eliza Swan
   Here's a health to the Battler of Montrose
   And the Diamond ship of fame
   We wear the trousers of the white
   And the jackets of the blue
   And when we return to Peterhead
   We'll have sweethearts anew

3. Along the quay at Peterhead
   The lasses stand around
   With their shawls all pulled around them
   And the salt tears runnin' down
   But don't you weep my bonnie lass
   Though you'll be left behind
   For the rose will bloom on Greenland's ice
   Before we change our mind

4. It will be bright both day and night
   When the Greenland lads come home
   With a ship that's full of oil me boys
   And money to our names
   We'll make the cradles for to rock
   And the blankets for to tear
   Aye and every lass in Peterhead sing
   Hushabye my dear

From the singing of Rob Paterson and The Easy Club

BOSTON HARBOR

From Bos-ton Har-bor we set sail, the wind was a blowin' a de-vil of a gale. With our
ring-tail set all a-baft the mizzen peak and our dolphin stri-ker plowing up the deep. WITH A
BIG BOW WOW TOW ROW ROW FOL - DE - ROL DE - RI - DOL DAY.

1. From Boston Harbor we set sail
   The wind was a-blowin' a devil of a gale
   With our ringtail set all abaft the mizzen peak
   And our dolphin striker plowing up the deep

   WITH A BIG BOW WOW, TOW ROW ROW
   FOL-DE-ROL DE-RI-DOL DAY

2. Our captain comes up from down below
   He looks aloft and he looks alow
   Well he looks alow and he looks aloft
   Saying coil your ropes there fore and aft

3. Back to his cabin he quickly crawls
   And unto his steward he loudly bawls
   Go bring me a glass that will make me cough
   For it's better weather here than it is up aloft

4. It's we poor sailors are standing on the deck
   With the blasted rain all a-pouring down our necks
   Not a drop of grog will he to us afford
   But he damns our eyes with every other word

5. Now there's one plan we sailors have
   Is for him to find a watery grave
   We'll shove him down in a deep dark hole
   Where the sharks'll have his body and the devil take
       his soul

From the singing of Joe Hickerson, Jeff Warner, Gerret Warner
and Tony Saletan

BRING 'EM DOWN

In Li - ver - pool I was born. BRING 'EM DOWN. But

Lon - don is me home from home. BRING 'EM DOWN. Them

Ro - ther - hide girls are might - y fine. BRING 'EM DOWN. They're

ne - ver a day be - hind the time. BRING 'EM DOWN. It's

around Cape Horn we all must go. BRING 'EM DOWN. A -

round Cape Stiff in the frost and snow. BRING 'EM DOWN.

Up the coast to Val - la - pol. BRING 'EM DOWN.

North - ward to Cal - la - o. BRING 'EM DOWN. Them

Cal - la - o girls I do a - dore. BRING 'EM DOWN. They

takes it all and asks for more. BRING 'EM DOWN. But them

Vall - a - pol girls puts on a show. BRING 'EM DOWN. They

wri - ggle their ass for the roll and go. BRING 'EM DOWN. It's

back home to Li - ver - pool. BRING 'EM DOWN.

Spend me pay like a blood - y fool. BRING 'EM DOWN. Them

Li - ver - pool girls I do ad - mire. BRING 'EM DOWN. They

sets your rig - ging all a - fire. BRING 'EM DOWN. I'm

Li - ver - pool born and bred. BRING 'EM DOWN.

Thick in the arm and thick in the head. BRING 'EM DOWN. So

rock and roll me ov - er boys. BRING 'EM DOWN.

Get the damn job o - ver boys. BRING 'EM DOWN

1. In Liverpool I was born
    BRING 'EM DOWN
    But London is me home from home
    BRING 'EM DOWN

2. Them Rotherhide girls are mighty fine
    They're never a day behind the time

3. It's around Cape Horn we all must go
    Around Cape Stiff in the frost and snow

4. Up the coast to Vallapol
    Northward to Callao

5. Them Callao girls I do adore
    They takes it all and asks for more

6. But them Vallapol girls puts on a show
    They wriggle their ass for the roll and go

7. It's back home to Liverpool
    Spend me pay like a bloody fool

8. Them Liverpool girls I do admire
    They sets your rigging all afire

9. I'm Liverpool born and bred
    Thick in the arm and thick in the head

10. So rock and roll me over boys
    Get the damn job over boys

From the singing of Louis Killen

BULLY IN THE ALLEY

1. Sally is the girl that I love dearly
   WAY HEY BULLY IN THE ALLEY
   Sally is the girl that I spliced nearly
   BULLY DOWN IN SHINBONE ALLEY

   So help me pump (PUMP) BULLY IN THE ALLEY
   WAY HEY BULLY IN THE ALLEY
   Help me pump (PUMP) BULLY IN THE ALLEY
   BULLY DOWN IN SHINBONE ALLEY

2. Seven longs years I've courted Sally
   All she did was dilly dally

3. Sally Brown I took a notion
   To sail across this damn wide ocean

4. Well I'll leave Sal and I'll go sailin'
   Leave my gal and I'll go whalin'

CAPE COD GIRLS

1. Cape Cod girls don't use no combs
   HAUL AWAY, HAUL AWAY
   Well they comb their hair with a codfish bone
   AND WE'RE BOUND AWAY FOR AUSTRALIA

   SO HEAVE HER UP MY BULLY BULLY BOYS
   HAUL AWAY, HAUL AWAY
   HEAVE HER UP AND DON'T YOU MAKE A NOISE
   AND WE'RE BOUND AWAY FOR AUSTRALIA

2. And the Cape Cod girls don't have no sleds
   Well they slide down a hill on a codfish head

3. And the Cape Cod cats don't have no tails
   Well they lost them all in a northeast gale

4. And the Cape Cod ladies don't have no frills
   Well they're plain and skinny like a codfish tail

5. Well the Cape Cod doctors don't use no pills
   Well they just give their patients old codfish gills

From the singing of David Marston, Charles O'Hegarty and David Jones (The Starboard List)

THE COAST OF BARBARY

1. Now there was two jolly ships
   From out of England came
   BLOW HIGH BLOW LOW, AND SO SAIL WE
   One she was the Queen of Russia
   And the other Prince of Wales
   CRUISING DOWN ALONG THE COAST OF BARBARY

2. Step aloft, step aloft
   Did our jolly bosun cry
   Look ahead and look astern
   At the weather look alee
   AND LOOK OUT ALONG…

3. Well there is no ship astern
   And there is no ship alee
   But there's a lofty ship to windward
   She's a sailing fast and free
   SHE'S A SAILING DOWN ALONG…

4. So to hail her, to hail her
   Did our jolly captain cry
   For he is man-of-war
   Or a privateer says he
   AND THEY'RE CRUISING DOWN ALONG…

5. I am not no man-of-war
   Nor a privateer says he
   But I am a saucy pirate
   I'm a-seeking for me fee
   I'M A-SEEKING DOWN ALONG…

6. So a broadside, a broadside
   All along with her we lay
   'Til at length the Queen of Russia
   Blew that pirate's mast away
   CRUISING DOWN ALONG…

7. And for quarter, for quarter
   The jolly pirate cried
   Oh the quarter I will give you
   I will sink you in the tide
   I WILL SINK YOU DOWN ALONG…

8. So we tied 'em up by twos
   And we tied 'em up by threes
   Yes we tied 'em up by dozens
   And we chucked 'em in the sea
   YES WE DROWNED 'EM DOWN ALONG…

From the singing of Peter Bellamy

THE DARK-EYED SAILOR

1. As I roved out one evening fair
   It being the summer time to take the air
   I spied a sailor and a lady gay
   And I stood to listen
   And I stood to listen to hear what they would say

2. He said fair lady why do you roam
   For the day is spent and the night is on
   She heaved a sigh while the tears did roll
   For my dark-eyed sailor
   For my dark-eyed sailor so young and stout and bold

3. 'Tis seven long years since he left this land
   A ring he took from off his lily-white hand
   One half of the ring is still here with me
   But the other's rollin'
   But the other's rollin' at the bottom of the sea

4. He said you may drive him out of your mind
   Some other young man you will surely find
   Love turns aside and soon cold has grown
   Like the winter's morning
   Like the winter's morning the hills are white with snow

5. She said I'll never forsake my dear
   Although we're parted this many a year
   Genteel he was and a rake like you
   To induce a maiden
   To induce a maiden to slight the jacket blue

6. One half of the ring did young William show
   She ran distracted in grief and woe
   Sayin' William, William, I have gold in store
   For my dark-eyed sailor
   For my dark-eyed sailor has proved his honor so

7. And there is a cottage by yonder lea
   This couple's married and does agree
   So maids be loyal when your love's at sea
   For a cloudy morning
   For a cloudy morning brings in a sunny day

From the singing of Gay Woods and Maddy Prior
(Steeleye Span)

DOCKYARD GATE

1. Come all you married seamen bold
   A few lines to you I'll write
   Just to let you know how the game do go
   When you are out of sight
   Just to let you know how the lads on shore
   Go sporting with your wives
   While you are on the rolling seas
   And venturing your sweet lives

2. It's now our ship is outward bound
   And ready for to sail
   May the heavens above protect my love
   With a sweet and pleasant gale
   And keep you clear all from the shore
   And never to return
   Until his pockets are well lined
   And then he's welcome home

3. A last farewell she takes of him
   And she begins to cry
   A-taking out her handkerchief
   To wipe her weeping eyes
   Me husband's gone to sea she cries
   How hard it is my case
   But still on shore there's plenty more
   Another will take his place

4. Then she goes to her fancy man
   These words to him did say
   Me husband he is gone to sea
   Tomorrow is half-pay day
   And you must wait at the dockyard gate
   Until that I come out
   For that very day we'll sweat his half-pay
   And drink both ale and stout

5. That day they spent in sweet content
   'Til the half-pay was no more
   Then never mind my dear she cries
   He's working hard for more
   Perhaps he's at the masthead
   A-dying with the cold
   Or perhaps he's at his watch on deck
   Our joys he can't behold

6. And now our ship she's homeward bound
   Brought up in Plymouth Sound
   She hears the gun me husband's come
   To him I must go down
   She goes unto her neighbor's house
   One thing of you I crave
   Lend me your gown for mine's in pawn
   It's the only one I have

7. Then she goes down unto the Sound
   And tries for to get in
   She so loudly for her husband calls
   And runs and kisses him
   Saying how happy we shall be my dear
   Now you are safe on shore
   You shall sit at home with me my love
   And go to sea no more

From the singing of John Jones and the Oyster Band

DONKEY RIDING

1. Was you ever in Quebec
   Stowing timber on the deck
   Where you breaks your bleeding neck
   RIDING ON A DONKEY

   WAY HEY AND AWAY WE GO
   DONKEY RIDING, DONKEY RIDING
   WAY HEY AND AWAY WE GO
   RIDING ON A DONKEY

2. Or was you ever in Timbuktoo
   Where them gals is black and blue
   And they waggle their backsides too
   RIDING…

3. Or was you ever in Vallapol
   Where them gals put on a show
   Waggle and wriggle with a roll and go
   RIDING…

4. Or was you ever in Canton
   Where the men wear pigtails long
   And the girls play honky-kong
   RIDING…

5. Or was you ever in Brumelow
   Where the Yanks is all the go
   And the gals dance heel to toe
   RIDING…

6. Or was you ever in Mobile Bay
   Screwing cotton all the day
   Where you works for little pay
   RIDING…

7. Or was you ever in Frisco Bay
   Where the girls they shout hooray
   Saying here comes Johnny with his three year pay
   RIDING…

From the singing of Bob Kotta (Howling Gael)

DRUNKEN SAILOR

1. What shall we do with a drunken sailor
   WHAT SHALL WE DO WITH A DRUNKEN SAILOR
   WHAT SHALL WE DO WITH A DRUNKEN SAILOR
   EARLY IN THE MORNING

   WAY HEY AND UP SHE RISES
   WAY HEY AND UP SHE RISES
   WAY HEY AND UP SHE RISES
   EARLY IN THE MORNING

2. Shave his belly with a rusty razor…

3. Put him in the scuppers with a hose pipe up him…

4. Put him in the bilge and make him drink it…

5. Put him in bed with the captain's daughter…

6. You ain't seen the captain's daughter…

7. She looks like an orangutang…

8. There she goes swinging through the rigging…

9. That's what we do with a drunken sailor…

THE EBENEZER

1. I shipped on board of the Ebenezer
   Ev'ry day 'twas scrub and grease her
   Send us aloft to scrape 'er down
   And if we growl they'll knock us down

   OH GET ALONG BOYS
   GET ALONG DO
   HANDY ME BOYS, SO HANDY
   GET ALONG BOYS
   GET ALONG DO
   HANDY ME BOYS, SO HANDY

2. The old man was a drunken geezer
   He couldn't sail the Ebenezer
   Learnt his trade on a Chinese junk
   He'd spend most time sir in his bunk

3. The first mate's name was Dickie Green sir
   The dirtiest bugger you've ever seen sir
   Walkin' the poop with a bucko roll
   May the sharks have his body and the devil take his
       soul

4. A Boston buck was second greaser
   He used to ship in Limejuice ships sir
   The Limey packets got too hot
   He jumped 'em and he cursed the lot

5. Well the bosun hailed from Tennessee sir
   He always wore a Blackball cheeser
   He had a gal in every port
   At least that's what his missus thought

6. The Ebenezer was so old sir
   She knew Columbus as a boy sir
   'Twas pump her bullies night and day
   To help her get to Liverpool Bay

7. Wet hash it was our only grub sir
   For breakfast, dinner and for supper
   The bread was tough as any brass
   And the meat was as salty as Lot's wife's ass

ESSEKEEBA RIVER

1. The Essekeeba River is the queen of rivers all
   BUDDY TA NA NA, WE ARE SOMEBODY OH
   The Essekeeba river is the queen of rivers all
   BUDDY TA NA NA, WE ARE SOMEBODY OH

   SOMEBODY, OH BODY, SOMEBODY, OH
   BUDDY TA NA NA, WE ARE SOMEBODY OH
   SOMEBODY, OH BODY, SOMEBODY, OH
   BUDDY TA NA NA, WE ARE SOMEBODY OH

2. The Essekeeba cap'ns is the king of cap'ns all

3. The Essekeeba bosuns is the king of bosuns all

4. The Essekeeba sailors is the chief of sailors all

5. The Essekeeba judies is the queen of judies all

From the singing of Earl Richards

FARE THEE WELL YOU BARBARY MERCHANTS

1. I promised her rings for her fingers
   Sparkling flowers for her flaxen hair
   I swore that I'd never set sail in foul weather
   But stay by her side on the shore

   FARE THEE WELL YOU BARBARY MERCHANTS
   FARE THEE WELL TO THE SPANISH BLOCKADE
   FARE THEE WELL TO THE STRAITS OF GIBRALTAR
   AND THE TREACHEROUS SEAS OF CATHAY

2. I gave her my promise to marry
   And took her sweet vow in return
   I swore that I'd never set sail in foul weather
   But stay by her side on the shore

3. I built her a cottage in Chatham
   Gave her children to sit by the fire
   I swore that I'd never set sail in foul weather
   But stay by her side on the shore

4. But a cottage is too small for a sailor
   Without the blue sea and the sky
   Though I swore that I'd never set sail in foul weather
   I left her behind on the shore

(last chorus)
TAKE ME BACK OH YOU BARBARY MERCHANTS
LET ME RISK THE SPANISH BLOCKADE
CARRY ME TO THE STRAITS OF GIBRALTAR
AND THE TREACHEROUS SEAS OF CATHAY

From the singing of Richard Chamberlain

FAREWELL NANCY

1. Farewell my lovely Nancy
   For I must now leave you
   Unto the salt seas I am bound for to go
   But let my long absence
   Be no trouble to you
   For I will return in the spring as you know

2. Like some pretty little seaboy
   I will dress and go with you
   In the deepest of dangers I shall stand your friend
   In the cold stormy weather
   When the winds they are a-blowin'
   My love I'll be willin' to wait on you then

3. Your pretty little hands
   Cannot handle our tackle
   Your pretty little feet to our topmast can't go
   And the cold stormy weather love
   You never could endure
   Therefore lovely Nancy to the sea do not go

From the singing of Tim Hart & Maddy Prior

FAREWELL TO NOVA SCOTIA

1. The sun was setting in the west
   The birds were singing on every tree
   All nature seemed inclined to rest
   But still there was no rest for me.

   FAREWELL TO NOVA SCOTIA
   THE SEA-BOUND COAST
   LET YOUR MOUNTAINS
   DARK AND DREARY BE
   FOR WHEN I AM FAR AWAY
   ON THE BRINY OCEAN TOSSED
   WILL YOU EVER HEAVE A SIGH
   AND A WISH FOR ME

2. I grieve to leave my native land
   I grieve to leave my comrades all
   My aging parents who I always held so dear
   And the bonnie, bonnie lass I do adore

3. The drums are beating the wars to alarm
   The captain calls and we must obey
   So farewell, farewell to Nova Scotia's charms
   But it's early in the morning I am far, far away

4. I have three brothers and they're at rest
   Their arms are folded upon their breast
   But a poor simple sailor just like me
   Must be tossed and driven on the dark blue sea

From the singing of Claudine Langille (Touchstone)

FAREWELL TO TARWATHIE

(George Scroggie, c.1850)

1. Farewell to Tarwathie
   Adieu Mormond Hills
   And the dear land of Crimond
   I bid ye farewell
   We're bound out for Greenland
   And ready to sail
   In hopes to find riches
   In hunting the whale

2. Adieu to my comrades
   For a while we must part
   And likewise the dear lass
   Who fair won my heart
   And the cold ice of Greenland
   My love will not chill
   And the longer my absence
   More loving she'll feel

3. Our ship is well-rigged
   And she's ready to sail
   Our crew they are anxious
   To follow the whale
   Where the icebergs do float
   And the stormy winds do blow
   Where the land and the ocean
   Is covered in snow

4. Oh the cold coast of Greenland
   Is barren and bare
   No seedtime or harvest
   Is ever known there
   And the birds here sing sweetly
   On mountain and dale
   But there isn't a birdie
   To sing to the whale

5. There is no habitation
   For a man to live there
   And the king of that country
   Is the fierce Greenland bear
   And there'll be no temptation
   To tarry long there
   With our ship bumper full
   We will homeward repair

From the singing of A.L. Lloyd

FIDDLERS' GREEN

(John Conolly)

1. As I roved by the dockside one evening so rare
    To view the still waters and take the salt air
    I heard an old fisherman singing this song
    Oh take me away boys me time is not long

    DRESS ME UP IN ME OILSKINS AND JUMPER
    NO MORE ON THE DOCKS I'LL BE SEEN
    JUST TELL ME OLD SHIPMATES
    I'M TAKING A TRIP, MATES
    AND I'LL SEE YOU SOMEDAY IN FIDDLERS' GREEN

2. Now Fiddlers' Green is a place I've heard tell
   Where fishermen go if they don't go to Hell
   Where the weather is fair and the dolphins do play
   And the cold coast of Greenland is far, far away

3. The sky's always clear and there's never a gale
   And the fish jump on board with a flip of their tails
   You can lie at your leisure there's no work to do
   And the Skipper's below making tea for the crew

4. And when you're in dock and the long trip is through
   There's pubs and there's clubs and there's lasses there
      too
   The girls are all pretty and the beer is all free
   And there's bottles of rum growing on every tree

5. Now I don't want a harp nor a halo not me
   Just give me a breeze and a good rolling sea
   And I'll play me old squeezebox as we sail along
   With the wind in the rigging to sing me this song

From the singing of John Conolly

FIRE MARENGO

1. Lift him up and carry him along
   FIRE MARENGO FIRE AWAY
   Put him down where he belongs
   FIRE MARENGO FIRE AWAY

2. Ease him down and let him lay
   Throw him in and there he'll stay

3. Stow him in his hull below
   It's stay he must and there he'll go

4. When I get back to Liverpool Town
   I'll haul a line to little Sally Brown

5. I'll haul her high and I'll haul her low
   I'll bust her blocks and I'll make her go

6. Sally she's a pretty little craft
   Shot to the fore and rounded aft

7. Rockin' chain'll raise the cry
   Bloody topmast sheave is dry

8. Screw the cotton screw him down
   Let's get the hell from Hilo town

From the singing of John Jones

THE FIRESHIP

As I strolled out one ev-en-ing all for a night's ca-reer. I spied a lof-ty clip-per ship and to her I did steer. I hoist-ed up my sig-a-nal, which she did quick-ly view. And when she saw my bunt-ing fly she im-me-diat-ely hove to. SHE HAD A DARK AND A RO-VING EYE AND HER HAIR HUNG DOWN IN RING-LETS. SHE WAS A NICE GIRL, A DE-CENT GIRL BUT ONE OF THE RA-KISH KIND.

1. As I strolled out one evening
   For a night's career
   I spied a lofty clipper ship
   And to her I did steer
   I hoisted up my signal
   Which she did quickly view
   And when she saw my bunting fly
   She immediately hove to

   SHE HAD A DARK AND ROVING EYE
   AND HER HAIR HUNG DOWN IN RINGLETS
   SHE WAS A NICE GIRL, A DECENT GIRL
   BUT ONE OF THE RAKISH KIND

2. Excuse me sir she said to me
   For being out so late
   For if me parents knew of it
   Then sad would be my fate
   Me father he's a minister
   A true and honest man
   Me mother she's a dancing girl
   And I do the best I can

3. I eyed that girl both up and down
   For I'd heard such talk before
   And when she moored herself to me
   I knew she was a whore
   But still she was a comely wench
   Her lips a ruby red
   Her bosom full her hips so slim
   She coyly hung her head

4. I took her to a tavern
   And treated her with wine
   But little did I think
   That she belonged to the rakish kind
   I handled her I dandled her
   But much to my surprise
   She was nothing but a fireship
   Rigged up in a disguise

5. So up the stairs and into bed
   I took that maiden fair
   I fired off my cannon
   Into her hatch so fair
   I fired off a broadside
   Until my shot was spent
   Then rammed that fireship's waterline
   Until my ram was bent

6. Then in the morning she was gone
   My money was gone too
   My clothes she'd hocked my watch she stole
   My sea bag bid adieu
   But she'd left behind a souvenir
   I'd have you all to know
   And in nine days to my surprise
   There was fire down below

7. So listen all you sailormen
   Who sail upon the sea
   And all you jolly prentice lads
   A warning take from me
   Steer clear of lofty fireships
   For me they left well spent
   For one burnt all me money up
   And left me broke and bent

FISH IN THE SEA

1. Come all you young sailor men listen to me
   I'll sing you a song of the fish in the sea

   AND IT'S WINDY WEATHER BOYS
   STORMY WEATHER BOYS
   WHEN THE WIND BLOWS
   WE'RE ALL TOGETHER BOYS
   BLOW YE WINDS WESTERLY
   BLOW YE WINDS BLOW
   JOLLY SOU'WESTER BOYS
   STEADY SHE GOES

2. Up jumps the eel with his slippery tail
   Climbs up aloft and reefs the topsail

3. Then up jumps the shark with his nine rows of teeth
   Saying you eat the dough boys and I'll eat the beef

4. Up jumps the whale the largest of all
   If you want any wind well I'll blow ye a squall

THE FIVE GALLON JAR

1. On the Barbary Coast there lived a man
   Old Larry was his name
   And in the days of the Cape Horn trade
   He played the shanghai game
   His wife's name was Mary Ann
   Sailors knew both near and far
   They never missed a lucky chance
   To use the big stone jar

   IN THE OLD VIRGINIA LOWLANDS, LOWLANDS LOW
   IN THE OLD VIRGINIA LOWLANDS LOW

2. Shellbacks and farmers just the same
   Sailed into Larry Marr's
   And sailed away around the Horn
   Helped by the big stone jar
   There were five or six drunken shellbacks
   Standing in before the bar
   Mrs. and Larry would prime the beer
   From the big five gallon jar

3. On the Barbary Coast their names is known
   As in old Larry Marr's
   For the dope that they served out to Jack
   From the big five gallon jar
   A hellship she was short of hands
   Of full red-blooded tars
   Mrs. and Larry would prime the beer
   From the big five gallon jar

4. From the Barbary Coast steer clear me boys
   And from old Larry Marr's
   Or else damn soon shanghaied you'll be
   With the old five gallon jar
   Shanghaied away on a skysail ship
   Around Cape Horn so far
   Goodbye to all the boys and girls
   And Larry's five gallon jar

From the singing of Bernard Wrigley

FLASH FRIGATE

1. 'Twas on a flash frigate
   Flash frigate of fame
   We sailed to the Indies
   La Pique was her name
   We suffered bad usage
   Of every degree
   And we worked just like slaves
   As we ploughed the salt sea

   DERRY DOWN DOWN
   DOWN DERRY DOWN

2. At four in the morning
   Our work does begin
   In our 'tween decks I'll tell you
   A bucket might swim
   Our main and top foremen
   So loudly do bawl
   For sand and for holystone
   Both great and small

3. Now our bosun comes up boys
    We know him so well
    He struts on the deck
    And he makes a great swell
    It's up on them yards boys
    Or God damn your eyes
    I've a pump handle here
    For to trim down your size

4. Your quids of tobacco
    Brave boys you must mind
    If you spit on the deck
    It's your death warrant signed
    If you spit over bow
    Over gangway or stern
    You're sure of three dozen
    To help you to learn

5. Come all brother seamen
    Wherever you be
    From the frigate La Pique
    I would have you keep free
    For you'll work and you'll sweat
    But you ain't worth a damn
    And you'll get sent half dead
    Back to merry England

From the singing of Louis Killen

THE FRISCO SHIP

1. Our ship she lies by Frisco Bay
   TO ME WAY HEY HO HIGH-O
   Our ship she lies by Frisco Bay
   A LONG TIME AGO

2. A smart Yankee packet lay out in the bay
   A-waiting the wind for to get underway

3. We sailed from Frisco in a full-rigged ship
   We sailed from Frisco in a full-rigged ship

4. Her masts was silver her yards was gold
   Her masts was silver her yards was gold

5. We're bound for New York with a cargo of gold
   Bound south 'round the Horn through the ice and
   the cold

6. If I ever gets to me feet on the shore
   I'll be the bosun of a little rum store

7. As soon as I gets to me feet on the land
   I'll ship as some young lady's fancy man

8. Oh a long time and a very long time
   It's a very long time since I wrote this rhyme

From the singing of Dick Holdstock and Allan MacLeod

GENERAL TAYLOR

1. General Taylor gained the day
   WALK HIM ALONG, JOHN CARRY HIM ALONG
   Oh General Taylor gained the day
   CARRY HIM TO HIS BURYING GROUND

   TO ME WAY, HAY, YOU STORMY
   WALK HIM ALONG, JOHN CARRY HIM ALONG
   TO ME WAY, HAY, YOU STORMY
   CARRY HIM TO HIS BURYING GROUND

2. We'll dig his grave with a silver spade
   And his shroud of the softest silk is made

3. We'll lower him down on a golden chain
   On every link we'll carve his name

4. Oh I wish I was General Taylor's son
   I'd build me a ship of ten thousand ton

5. Well I'd build me a ship of ten thousand ton
   I'd fill her up with Barbados rum

6. I'd give out a bottle to every hand
   And a barrel full for the shantyman

7. Oh General Taylor he died long ago
   He died long ago down in old Mexico

From the singing of Tim Hart and Steeleye Span
and Louis Killen

THE GLENDY BURK

(Stephen Foster)

1. The Glendy Burk is a mighty fast boat
   With a might fast captain too
   He sits up there on the hurricane roof
   And he keeps his eye on the crew
   I can't stay here for they work too hard
   I'm bound to leave this town
   I'll take my duds and tote 'em on my back
   When the Glendy Burk comes down

   HO! FOR LOUISIANA!
   I'M BOUND TO LEAVE THIS TOWN
   I'LL TAKE MY DUDS AND TOTE 'EM ON MY BACK
   WHEN THE GLENDY BURK COMES DOWN

2. The Glendy Burk has a funny old crew
   And they sing the boatman's song
   They burn the pitch and the pine knot too
   For to shove the boat along
   The smoke goes up and the engine roars
   And the wheel goes round and round
   So fare you well for I'll take a little ride
   When the Glendy Burk comes down

3. I'll work all night in the wind and storm
   I'll work all day in the rain
   Till I find myself on the levy dock
   In New Orleans again
   They make me mow in the hay field here
   And knock my head with the flail
   I'll go where they work with the sugar and the cane
   And roll on the cotton bale

4. My lady love is as pretty as a pink
   I'll meet her on the way
   I'll take her back to the sunny old South
   And there I'll make her stay
   So don't you fret my honey dear
   Oh don't you fret Miss Brown
   I'll take you back 'fore the middle of the week
   When the Glendy Burk comes down

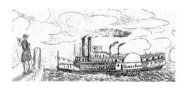

THE GOLDEN VANITEE

1. There once was a captain
   Who was boasting on the quay
   Oh I have a ship
   And a gallant ship is she
   Of all the ships I know
   Well she is the best for me
   And she's sailin' in the lowlands low

   IN THE LOWLANDS, LOWLANDS
   (AND SHE'S SAILIN' IN THE LOWLANDS LOW) ETC.

2. Well I had her built
   In the North country
   And I had her christened
   The Golden Vanitee
   I armed her and I manned her
   And I sent her off to sea
   And she's sailin' in the lowlands low

3. Well then up stepped a sailor
   Who was just returned from sea
   Oh I was aboard
   Of the Golden Vanitee
   When we was held and chased
   By a Spanish piratee
   And we sank 'em in the lowlands low

4. Well we had aboard of us
   A little cabin boy
   Who said what will you give-a me
   If the galley I destroy
   I'll give to you me daughter
   Oh she is me pride and joy
   If you sink 'em in the lowlands low

5. So the boy bared his breast
   And he plunged into the tide
   He swam until he came
   To the rascal pirate's side
   He climbed aboard he went below
   By none was he espied
   And he sank 'em in the lowlands low

6. Oh well he bored with his auger
   He bored once or twice
   Some was playing cards
   And some was playing dice
   But when he let the water in
   It dazzled at their eyes
   And he sank 'em in the lowlands low

7. So then the cabin boy he swam
   Unto the starboard side
   Saying captain take me up
   For I am drowning in the tide
   I'll shoot you and I'll kill you
   If you claim me child as bride
   And I'll sink you in the lowlands low

8. So then the cabin boy he swam
   Unto the larboard side
   Saying messmates take me up
   For I am drifting with the tide
   They took him up so quickly
   But when on deck he died
   And they buried him in the lowlands low

9. Oh yes they took him up so quickly
   But when on deck he died
   They sewed him in his hammock
   That was so strong and wide
   They said a short prayer over him
   And they dropped him in the tide
   And they sailed from the lowlands low

10. Here's a curse unto the captain
    Wherever he may be
    For taking that poor cabin boy
    So far away to sea
    For taking that poor cabin boy
    So far away to sea
    And to leave him in the lowlands low

From the singing of Tony Rose
(Rory Block also sings an amazing version of this song)

THE GOOD SHIP KANGAROO

(Harry Clifton, 1856)

Once I was a waiting man who lived at home at ease.

Now I am a mariner that ploughs the angry seas. I

always loved a seafaring life I bid me love adieu. I

shipped as steward and cook me boys on board the Kangaroo. Oh I

NEVER THOUGHT SHE WOULD PROVE FALSE OR EITHER PROVE UNTRUE, AS WE

SAILED AWAY FROM MILFORD BAY ON BOARD THE KANGAROO.

1. Once I was a waiting man
    Who lived at home at ease
    Now I am a mariner
    That ploughs the angry seas
    I always loved seafaring life
    I bid me love adieu
    I shipped as steward and cook me boys
    On board the Kangaroo

    OH I NEVER THOUGHT SHE WOULD PROVE FALSE
    OR EITHER PROVE UNTRUE
    AS WE SAILED AWAY FROM MILFORD BAY
    ON BOARD THE KANGAROO

2. Think of me, oh think of me
   She mournfully did say
   When you are in a foreign land
   And I am far away
   And take this lucky thrupenny bit
   It will make you bear in mind
   This loving trusting faithful heart
   You left in tears behind

3. Cheer up, cheer up my own true love
   Don't weep so bitterly
   She sobbed she sighed she choked she cried
   'Til she could not say goodbye
   I won't be gone for very long
   But for a month or two
   And when I will return again
   Of course I'll visit you

4. Our ship it was homeward bound
   From manys the foreign shore
   And manys the foreign present
   Unto my love I bore
   I brought tortoises from Tenerife
   And ties from Timbuktu
   A China rat and a Bengal cat
   And a Bombay cockatoo

5. Paid off I sought her dwelling
   On the street above the town
   Where an ancient dame upon the line
   Was hanging out her gown
   Where is my love, she's vanished sir
   About six months ago
   With a smart young man who drives the van
   For Chaplin Son & Co.

6. Here's a health to dreams of married life
   To soap suds and blue
   Heart's true love, patent starch
   And washing soda too
   I'll go into some foreign shore
   No longer can I stay
   With some China Hottentot
   I'll throw my life away

7. My love she was no foolish girl
   Her age it was two score
   My love she was no spinster
   She'd been married twice before
   I cannot say it was her wealth
   That stole my heart away
   She was a washer in the laundry
   For one and nine a day

From the singing of Christy Moore and Planxty

GOODBYE FARE THEE WELL

1. Oh we're homeward bound to Liverpool town
   GOOD BYE, FARE THEE WELL
   GOOD BYE, FARE THEE WELL
   Well them Liverpool judies they all will come down
   HOORAH, ME BOYS, WE'RE HOMEWARD BOUND

2. Them gals there on Lime Street we soon hope to meet
   And soon we'll be a-rolling both sides of the street

3. We'll meet those fly girls and we'll ring the old bell
   With them judies we'll meet there we'll raise bloody
      hell

4. Then I'll tell me old woman when I gets back home
   The gals there on Lime Street won't leave me alone

5. We're homeward bound to the gals of the town
   So stamp up me bullies and heave it around

6. Oh we're homeward bound we'll have youse to know
   And over the water to Liverpool we'll go

From the singing of Louis Killen

THE GREENLAND WHALE FISHERIES

1. In the year of 1853
   And on June the 18th day
   We hoisted our flag
   To the top of the mast
   And for Greenland bore away brave boys
   And for Greenland bore away

2. Well the lookout he stood at the top of the mast
   With a spyglass in his hand
   There's a whale, there's a whale
   There's a whalefish he cried
   And she blows at every span brave boys
   And she blows at every span

3. Well the captain he stood on the quarter deck
   And the ice was in his eyes
   Overhaul, overhaul
   Let your jib sheets fall
   Go and put your boat to sea brave boys
   Go and put your boat to sea

4. Well the boat pulled out and the whale in full view
   With a single flourish of his tail
   He capsized our boat
   And four men were drowned
   And we never caught that whale brave boys
   And we never caught that whale

5. Oh the losing of those four gallant lads
   Well it grieved our captain sore
   But the losing of
   That great whale fish
   Well it grieved him ten times more brave boys
   Well it grieved him ten times more

6. Oh Greenland is a barren land
   It's a land that has no green
   But there's ice and there's snow
   Where the whale fishes blow
   And the daylight's seldom seen brave boys
   And the daylight's seldom seen

From the singing of Jim Kamas

THE HANDSOME CABIN BOY

1. 'Tis of a pretty female
   As you shall understand
   Her mind was set on roving
   Into some foreign land
   Attired in sailor's clothing
   She boldly did appear
   And engaged with a captain
   To serve him for one year

2. She engaged with the captain
   A cabin boy to be
   The wind stood fine and clearly
   And so they put to sea
   The captain's lady being on board
   She seemed for to enjoy
   So glad that the captain had engaged
   With a handsome cabin boy

3. Now so nimble was this pretty maid
   She did her duty well
   But mark what follows after
   The song it soon will tell
   By eating of the captain's biscuits
   Her color did destroy
   And the waist did swell of pretty Nell
   The handsome cabin boy

Pocket Shantyman

4. Now as through the Bay of Biscay
    Our gallant ship did plough
    One night among the sailors
    There was a pretty row
    They bundled from their hammocks
    Which did their rest destroy
    They swore about the groaning of
    The handsome cabin boy

5. Oh doctor, oh doctor
    The cabin boy did cry
    The sailors swore by all and one
    The cabin boy would die
    The doctor ran with all his might
    A-smiling at the fun
    To think that a sailor lad could have
    A daughter or a son

6. Now when the sailors all heard the joke
    They all began to stare
    The child belonged to none of them
    They solemnly declared
    The lady to the captain said
    Me lad I wish you joy
    For it was either you or I betrayed
    The handsome cabin boy

From the singing of Martin Carthy

HANGING JOHNNY

1. Oh they calls me Hanging Johnny
    AWAY BOYS AWAY
    They says I hangs for money
    SO HANG BOYS HANG

2. They says I hangs for money
    'Cause hanging is so funny

3. Oh first I hung me daddy
    And then I hung me mammy

4. Oh yes I hung me mother
    My sister and my brother

5. Oh then I hung me granny
    I hung her up quite canny

6. Oh I hung my sister Sally
    I hung the whole damn family

7. I'll hang all mates and skippers
    I'll hang 'em by their flippers

8. I'll hang the bloody copper
    I'll give him the long gropper

9. I'll hang the bloody bosun
    The dirty rotten whore's son

10. I'll hang all rotten liars
    I'd even hang a friar

11. A rope, a beam, a ladder
    I'll hang youse all together

12. Oh they calls me Hanging Johnny
    But I never hung nobody

From the singing of David Jones, David Marston and Charles O'Hegarty (The Starboard List)

HAUL AWAY FOR ROSIE-O

1. You can talk about your Boodle girls
   Like up-in-the-corner Sally

   AWAY, HAUL AWAY
   WE'LL HAUL AWAY FOR ROSIE
   AWAY, HAUL AWAY
   WE'LL HAUL WAY FOR ROSIE-O

2. There is none can push a jug
   Like the girls of Dogleg Alley

3. Once I had an Irish girl
   Her name was Kitty Flanagan

4. She stole me boots, she stole me purse
   She stole me plate and pannikin

5. Then I had a gypsy girl
   Her mother called her Molly

6. And sometimes she got drunk at nights
   And sometimes only jolly

7. Then I had an English girl
   She wasn't very sporty

8. And everything I asked her for
   She said it was too naughty

9. Then I had a Liverpool girl
   And when she got the notion

10. She'd rise and fall as steady as
    The waves upon the ocean

11. Once in my life I married a wife
    And damn her she was lazy

12. She wouldn't stay at home at night
    It damn near drove me crazy

13. Stayed out all night oh what a sight
    And where do you think I found her

14. Behind the pub with her sheets hauled up
    And twenty men around her

HAUL ON THE BOWLINE

Haul on the bow - lin', Kit - ty is me dar - lin'.

HAUL ON THE BOW - LIN', THE BOW - LIN' HAUL.

1. Haul on the bowlin', Kitty is me darlin'
   HAUL ON THE BOWLIN', THE BOWLIN' HAUL

2. Haul on the bowlin', Kitty comes from Liverpool

3. Haul on the bowlin', so early in the mornin'

4. Haul on the bowlin', and the old man he's a-growlin'

5. Haul on the bowlin', before she starts a-rollin'

6. Haul on the bowlin', but we don't know where we're going

7. Haul on the bowlin', and we don't know where we're sailing from

8. Haul on the bowlin', and the sooner we're get going

9. Haul on the bowlin', well the sooner we comes home again

10. Haul on the bowlin', it's a weary way to Liverpool

11. Haul on the bowlin', it's a far cry to payday

HEARTS OF GOLD

1. 'Twas the plowing of the raging seas
   It was always my delight
   But those loving old landlubbers
   No dangers do they know
   Not like we long Jack Hearts of Gold
   Who plow the ocean through
   Not like we long Jack Hearts of Gold
   Who plow the ocean through

2. They are always with the pretty girls
   A setting them fine treats
   And filling of their pretty heads
   With the work they've done in a corn field
   But the cutting of the grass and weeds
   It's all that they can do
   While we long Jack Hearts of Gold
   Plough the ocean through

3. And when the sun it does go down
   They must lay aside their plow
   And their work they can no longer stand
   It's homeward they must go
   And they take their suppers with content
   And into bed they crawl
   While we long Jack Hearts of Gold
   Stand many the bitter squall

4. The seas they run full mountains high
    Which toss us up and down
    We are in the midst of danger boys
    For fear our ship might found
    Oh but never be down-hearted boys
    We'll see our girls again
    In spite of all our enemies
    We will plow the raging main

5. We will sing to every port of land
    Which ever yet was known
    We will bring back gold and silver boys
    When we return to home
    And we'll make our courtships flourish boys
    When we arrive on shore
    And when our money is all gone
    We'll plow the seas for more

6. So come all you pretty damsels
    If the truth you only knew
    Of the dangers of the raging main
    From labors unto you
    You would have more contempt for them
    Than ever yet was known
    You would hate those loving landlubbers
    Who always stay at home

From the singing of William Pint and Felicia Dale

HEAVE AWAY ME JOHNNIES

1. There's some that's bound for New York town
   And some that's bound for France
   HEAVE AWAY ME JOHNNIES, HEAVE AWAY
   And there's some that's bound for the Bengal Bay
   For to teach them whales to dance
   HEAVE AWAY ME JOLLY BOYS
   WE'RE ALL BOUND TO GO

2. So the pilot he is awaiting for
   The turning of the tide
   And then me boys we'll be gone again
   With a good and a westerly wind

3. So it's fare you well all you Kingston girls
   Likewise St. Andrew's dock
   If ever we come back again
   We'll make your cradles rock

4. So come all you hardweather sailing men
   That round the Cape of Storms
   Be sure you got your oilskins on
   Or you'll wish that you'd never been born

From the singing of Royston Wood and Heather Wood

HEAVE YA HO

1. Man your boats and leave the Whale
   What care we for calm or gale
   Aye tak' a drink as lang as ye can
   Brandy's guid amang het ale

   HEAVE YA HO, AND AWAY WE GO
   HEAVE YA HO, AND AWAY-OH
   HEAVE YA HO, AND AWAY WE GO
   HEAVE YA HO, AND AWAY-OH

2. Wave tae yer lass, they're a' the same
   Mag an' Meg and Jeannie and Jane
   Oh how they laugh when we hae fish
   But oh how they girn when we hae nane

3. Lady Twynfords lang tails
   Comin' doon the brae-oh
   And she maun get a' the cream o' the milk
   An' we maun get a' the whey-oh

4. What care we for wind or storm
   What care we for gale-oh
   Gin we maun haul a' the creel ower the side
   We'll drink the milk o' the Whale-oh

From the singing of Davy Steele (Battlefield Band)

Pocket Shantyman

HENRY MARTIN

There were __ three bro - thers in mer - ry Scot - land. In
mer - ry Scot - land there were three. _____ And
they did cast lots which of them __ should go ____ should
go ____ should go. For to turn rob - ber all
on the salt sea. _____

1. There were three brothers in merry Scotland
   In merry Scotland there were three
   And they did cast lots which of them should go
   Should go, should go
   And turn robber all on the salt sea

2. The lot it fell first upon Henry Martin
   The youngest of all of the three
   That he should turn robber all on the salt sea
   The salt sea, the salt sea
   For to maintain his two brothers and he

3. They had not been sailing for a long winter's night
   And part of a short winter's day
   When they did espy a stout lofty ship
   Lofty ship, lofty ship
   Coming and bearing down on them straightway

4. Hello, hello, cried Henry Martin
   What makes you sail so nigh
   I'm a rich merchant ship bound for fair London Town
   London Town, London Town
   Would you please for to let us pass by

5. Oh no, oh no, cried Henry Martin
   This thing it never can be
   For I have turned robber all on the salt sea
   The salt sea, the salt sea
   For to maintain my two brothers and me

6. So lower your topsail and fire up your men
   Bring your ship under my lee
   For I have resolved for to pirate you here
   You here, you here
   For to maintain my two brothers and me

7. So broadside for broadside and at it they went
   For fully two hours or three
   'Til Henry Martin gave to them the death shot
   The death shot, the death shot
   And straight to the bottom went she

8. Sad news, sad news, to fair London came
   Sad news to fair London Town
   There's been a rich vessel and she's cast away
   Cast away, cast away
   And all of her merry men drowned

From the singing of Pamela Morgan (Figgy Duff)

HI-HO COME ROLL ME OVER

1. Oh-ho why don't you blow-o
   HI-HO COME ROLL ME OVER
   Oh-ho why don't you blow-o
   HI-HO COME ROLL ME OVER

2. One man to strike the bell
   One man to strike the bell

3. Two men to man the wheel
   Two men to man the wheel

4. Three men to'gallant braces
   Three men to'gallant braces

5. Four men to man the capstan
   Four men to man the capstan

6. Five men to heave the lead
   Five men to heave the lead

7. Six men to furl t'g'ns'ls
   Six men to furl t'g'ns'ls

8. Seven men to bunt a bo
   Seven men to bunt a bo

HOG EYE MAN

1. Oh hand me down my riding cane
   I'm off to meet my darlin' Jane

   AND A HOG-EYE
   RAILROAD NAVVY WITH HIS HOG-EYE
   STEADY ON A JIG WITH A HOG-EYE-O
   SHE WANTS THE HOG-EYE MAN

2. Oh the hog-eye man is the man for me
   Sailin' down from o'er the sea

3. Oh he come to the shack where Sally did dwell
   He knocked on the door he rung a bell

4. Oh who's been here since I been gone
   Railroad navvy with his sea-boots on

5. If I catch him here with Sally once more
   I'll sling me hook go to sea once more

6. Oh Sally's in the garden sifting sand
   Her hog-eye man sittin' hand in hand

7. Oh Sally's in the garden punchin' duff
   The cheeks of her arse go chuff, chuff, chuff

8. Oh I won't wear a hog-eye damned if I do
   Got jiggers in his feet and he can't wear shoes

9. Oh the hog-eye man is the man for me
   He is blind and he cannot see

10. Oh a hog-eye ship and a hog-eye crew
    A hog-eye mate and a skipper too

From the singing of Martin Carthy & Family

HOLY GROUND

1. Fare thee well my lovely Dinah
   A thousand times adieu
   For we're goin' away from the Holy Ground
   And the girls we all love true
   We'll sail the salt sea over
   And we'll return for shore
   To see again the girls we love
   And the Holy Ground once more

   (FINE GIRL YOU ARE)
   YOU'RE THE GIRL I DO ADORE
   AND STILL I LIVE IN HOPE TO SEE
   THE HOLY GROUND ONCE MORE
   (FINE GIRL YOU ARE)

2. And now the storm is raging
   And we are far from shore
   And the good old ship is tossing about
   And the riggin' is all tore
   And the secret of my mind my love
   You're the girl I do I adore
   And still I live in hope to see
   The Holy Ground once more

3. And now the storm is over
   And we are safe and well
   We will go into a public house
   And we sit and drink our fill
   We will drink strong ale and porter
   And we'll make the rafters roar
   And when our money is all spent
   We will go to sea once more

From the singing of The Clancy Brothers & Tommy Makem

HOME BOYS HOME

1. Well who wouldn't be a sailor lad
   A-sailing on the main
   To gain the good will
   Of his captain's good name
   He came to shore
   One evening for to see
   And that was the beginning
   Of my own true love and me

   AND IT'S HOME, BOYS, HOME (clap, clap)
   HOME I'D LIKE TO BE
   HOME FOR AWHILE IN ME OWN COUNTRY
   WHERE THE OAK AND THE ASH
   AND THE BONNY ROWAN TREE
   ARE ALL A-GROWING GREEN IN THE NORTH COUNTRY

Pocket Shantyman

2. Well I asked her for a candle
   To light me way to bed
   Likewise for a handkerchief
   To tie around me head
   She tendered to me needs
   Like a young maid ought to do
   So then I says to her now
   Won't you jump in with me too

3. Well she jumped into bed
   And making no alarm
   Thinking a young sailor lad
   Could do to her no harm
   I hugged her and I kissed her
   The whole night long
   'Til she wished the short night
   Had been seven years long

4. Well early next morning
   The sailor lad arose
   And into Mary's apron
   Threw a handful of gold
   Saying take this me dear
   For the damage that I've done
   For tonight I fear I've left you
   With a daughter or a son

5. And if it be a girl child
   Send her out to nurse
   With gold in her pocket
   And with silver in her purse
   But if it be a boy child
   He'll wear the jacket blue
   And go climbing up the rigging
   Like his daddy used to do

6. And so come all of you fair maidens
   A warning take by me
   Never let a sailor lad
   An inch above your knee
   I trusted one
   And he beguiled me
   He left me with a pair of twins
   That dangle on me knee

Pocket Shantyman

I WILL SET MY SHIP IN ORDER

1. I will set my ship in order
   I will sail her on the sea
   I'll go far over yonder border
   To see if my love minds on me
   He sailed east and he sailed west
   He sailed far, far seeking land
   'Til he came to his true love's window
   He knocked loud and would be in

2. Oh who is that at my bedroom window
   And knocks so loud and would be in
   'Tis I, 'tis I, your ain true lover
   And I am drenched untae my skin
   So go and go and ask your faither
   See if he'll let you marry me
   If he says no come back and tell me
   It's the last time I'll trouble thee

3. My father's in his chamber writing
   Setting down his merchandise
   In his hand he holds a letter
   That speaks much in your dispraise
   My mother's in her chamber sleeping
   Words of love she will not hear
   You may go and court another
   Whisper softly in her ear

4. Then she arose, put on her clothing
   It was to let her true love in
   E're she had the door unlockit
   His ship was sailing on the main
   Come back, come back, my ain dear Johnny
   Come back, come back and marry me
   How can I come back and marry you love
   The ship is sailing on the sea

5. Fish may fly and the seas run dry
   The rocks may melt doon wi' the sun
   The working man may forget his labor
   Before that my love returns again
   She's turned herself right roun' about
   She's flung herself intae the sea
   Farewell for aye, my ain dear Johnny
   Ye'll ne'er hae tae come back to me

From the singing of Tony Cuffe (Ossian)

I'LL GO AND 'LIST FOR A SAILOR

1. Oh list, oh list to me sorrowful lay
   And attention give to me song I pray
   When you've heard it all you'll say
   That I'm an unfortunate tailor

2. For once I was happy as a bird in a tree
   My Sarah was all in the world to me
   Now I'm cut out by a son of the sea
   And she's left me here to bewail her

3. Why did Sarah serve me so
   No more will I stitch and no more will I sew
   Me thimble and me needle to the winds I'll throw
   And I'll go and 'list for a sailor

4. Now me days were honey and me nights were the
      same
   'Til a man called Cobb from the ocean came
   With his long black beard and his muscular frame
   A captain on board of a whaler

5. Well he spent his money both frank and free
   With his tales of the land and his songs of the sea
   And he stole me Sarah's heart from me
   And blighted the hopes of a tailor

6. Well once I was with her when in came Cobb
   Avast he cried you blubbery swab
   If you don't knock off I'll scuttle your knob
   And Sarah smiled at the sailor

7. So now I'll cross the raging sea
   For Sarah's proved untrue to me
   Me heart's locked up and she's the key
   What a very unfeeling gaoler

8. And so now kind friends I'll bid you adieu
   No more me woes shall trouble you
   I'll travel the country through and through
   And go and 'list for a sailor

From the singing of John Kirkpatrick

I'LL GO TO SEA NO MORE

1. When first I came to Liverpool
    I went upon a spree
    And me money alas I spent it fast
    Got drunk as drunk could be
    And when me money it was all gone
    It's then I wanted more
    But a man must be blind to make up his mind
    To go to sea once more

    ONCE MORE, BOYS, ONCE MORE
    TO GO TO SEA ONCE MORE
    A MAN MUST BE BLIND TO MAKE UP HIS MIND
    TO GO TO SEA ONCE MORE

2. I spent the night with Angeline
   Too drunk to roll in bed
   And me watch was new and me money too
   And with 'em in the morning she fled
   And as I walked the streets about
   The whores they all would roar
   Here comes Jack Rapp the poor sailor lad
   He must go to sea once more

   ONCE MORE, BOYS, ONCE MORE
   HE MUST GO TO SEA ONCE MORE
   HERE COMES JACK RAPP THE POOR SAILOR LAD
   HE MUST GO TO SEA ONCE MORE

3. And as I walked the streets about
   I met with the Rapper Brown
   I asked him would he take me on
   He looked at me with a frown
   He said last time I paid you off
   With me you chalk no score
   But I'll give you the chance and I'll take your advance
   And I'll send you to see once more

   ONCE MORE, BOYS, ONCE MORE
   I'LL SEND YOU TO SEA ONCE MORE
   I'LL GIVE YOU A CHANCE AND I'LL TAKE YOUR ADVANCE
   AND I'LL SEND YOU TO SEA ONCE MORE

4. Well he booked me on to a whaling ship
   All bound for the arctic seas
   Where the ice and snow and the cold winds blow
   Jamaica rum would freeze
   And the worst to bear was I had no gear
   I'd lost all me money on shore
   It's then I wished that I was dead
   So I'd go to sea no more

NO MORE, BOYS, NO MORE
I'D GO TO SEA NO MORE
IT'S THEN I WISHED THAT I WAS DEAD
SO I'D GO TO SEA NO MORE

5. Sometimes we're catching whales me boys
   And sometimes catching none
   With a twenty foot oar all strokin' around
   'Til two o'clock in the morn
   And when the evening shadows fall
   We rest our weary oar
   And it's then I wished that I was dead
   Or safe with a girl on shore

   ON SHORE, BOYS, ON SHORE
   OR SAFE WITH A GIRL ON SHORE
   IT'S THEN I WISHED THAT I WAS DEAD
   OR SAFE WITH A GIRL ON SHORE

6. Come all you bold seafarin' men
   Come listen to my song
   Well when you come in from those long long trips
   I'd have you not go wrong
   Take my advice don't drink strong drink
   Or go sleeping with no whores
   Get married instead and spend all night in bed
   And don't go to sea no more

   NO MORE, BOYS, NO MORE
   DON'T GO TO SEA NO MORE
   GET MARRIED INSTEAD AND SPEND ALL NIGHT IN BED
   AND DON'T GO TO SEA NO MORE

From the singing of Bob Kotta (Howling Gael)

JIM JONES

Come and lis-ten for a mo-ment lads and hear me tell my tale, how a-
cross the sea from Eng - land I was con-demned to sail. Well the
ju - ry found me guil - ty and then the judge says he, oh for
life I'm send-ing you Jim Jones a - cross the stor-my sea. But
take a trip be-fore you ship to join the i - ron gang, don't
get too gay in Bo-ta-ny Bay or else you'll sure-ly hang. Or
else you'll sure-ly hang says he and af-ter that Jim Jones, oh it's
high up on the gal-lows tree the crows will pick your bones.

1. Now come listen for a moment lads
   And hear me tell me tale
   How across the sea from England
   I was condemned to sail
   Oh the jury said he's guilty
   and then says the judge says he
   Oh for life, Jim Jones, I'm sending you
   Across the stormy sea

And take a tip before you ship
To join the iron gang
Don't get too gay in Botany Bay
Or else you'll surely hang
Or else you'll hang he says says he
And after that Jim Jones
Oh way up upon the gallows tree
The crows will pick your bones

2. Well our ship was high upon the sea
When pirates came along
Oh but the soldiers on our convict ship
Were full five hundred strong
They opened fire and somehow drove
That pirate ship away
But I'd rather have joined that pirate ship
Than gone to Botany Bay

With storms a-crashing down on us
And the wind a blowing gale
I'd rather have drowned in misery
Than gone to New South Wales
There's no time for mischief there they said
Remember that they say
Oh they'll flog the poaching out of you
Out there in Botany Bay.

3. Well it's day and night the irons clang
And like poor galley slaves
Oh we toil and toil and when we die
Must fill dishonored graves
But by and by I'll slip me chains
And to the bush I'll go
And I'll join the brave bushrangers there
Jack Donahue and Co.

And some dark night when everything
Is silent in the town
I'll shoot the tyrants one and all
I'll gun the floggers down
Oh I'll give them all a little shock
Remember what I say
And they'll yet regret they sent Jim Jones
In chains to Botany Bay

From the singing of John Kirkpatrick

JOHN KANAKA

1. I thought I heard the old man say
   JOHN KANAKANAKA TOO-RI-AY
   Tomorrow is our sailing day
   JOHN KANAKANAKA TOO-RI-AY

   TOO-RI-AY, OH TOO-RI-AY
   JOHN KANAKANAKA TOO-RI-AY

2. I thought I heard the bosun say
   There's work tomorrow but no work today

3. The bosun says before you're through
   You'll curse your mother for having you

4. There's rotten meat and weevily bread
   It's pump or drown the old man said

5. She would not steer and she would not stay
   She shipped the water both night and day

6. It's one more pull and that will do
   For we're the bullies to pull her through

*From the singing of David Jones, David Marston and
Charles O'Hegarty (The Starboard List)*

JOLLY ROVING TAR

1. Ships may come and ships may go
    As long as the sea does roll
    Each sailor lad just like his dad
    He loves a flowing bowl
    A trip ashore he does adore
    With a girl that's plump and round
    When your money's gone it's the same old song
    Get up Jack, John sit down

    COME ALONG, COME ALONG
    ME JOLLY BRAVE BOYS
    THERE'S LOTS OF GROG IN THE JAR
    WE'LL PLOW THE BRINY OCEAN
    WITH A JOLLY ROVING TAR

2. When Jack's gets in it's then he'll steer
   For some old boarding house
   They'll welcome him with rum and gin
   They'll feed him on pork souse
   He'll lend and spend and not offend
   'Til he lies drunk on the ground
   When your money's gone it's the same old song
   Get up Jack, John sit down

3. He then will sail aboard some ship
   For India or Japan
   In Asia there the ladies fair
   All love the sailor men
   He'll go ashore and on a tear
   He'll buy some girl a gown
   When your money's gone it's the same old song
   Get up Jack, John sit down

4. When Jack gets old and weatherbeat
   Too old to roam about
   In some rum shop they'll let him stop
   'Til eight bells calls him out
   He'll raise his eyes up to the sky
   Sayin' boys we're homeward bound
   When your money's gone it's the same old song
   Get up Jack, John sit down

From the singing of Jeff Warner

THE KEEPER OF THE EDDYSTONE LIGHT

Me father was the keep-er of the Ed-dystone light, and he slept with a mermaid one fine night.

From this un-ion there sprang three, a por-poise a por-gy and the o-ther was me.

YO HO HO, THE WIND BLOWS FREE. HO FOR THE LIFE ON THE ROL - LING SEA.

1. Me father was the keeper of the Eddystone light
   And he slept with a mermaid one fine night
   From this union there sprang three
   A porpoise and a porgy and the other was me

   YO HO HO, THE WIND BLOWS FREE
   HO FOR THE LIFE ON THE ROLLING SEA

2. One day as I was a-trimming the glim
   Hummin' a tune from the evening hymn
   A voice from the starboard shouted ahoy
   And there was me mother a-sittin' on a buoy

3. Oh what has become of me children three
   Me mother then she asked of me
   One was exhibited as a talking fish
   The other was served in a chafing dish

4. Well the phosphorus flashed in her seaweed hair
   I looked again and me mother wasn't there
   But I heard her voice echoing back through the night
   The devil take the keeper of the Eddystone light

From the singing of the Barquentones

THE LADY LEROY

1. As I was a-walking one morning in May
   A-viewing wild flowers all Nature seemed gay
   I spied a young couple on Erin's green shore
   They were viewing the ocean where the wild billows
      roar

2. He said Pretty Polly you're the girl I adore
   For to be parted from you it grieves my heart sore
   Your parents are rich love and angry with me
   And if I tarry with you, I ruined will be

3. She's dressed herself up in a suit of men's clothes
   And to her old father immediately goes
   She's purchased a ship and laid down the demand
   It was little he knew it was his own daughter's hand

4. She went to her true love and this she did say
   Rise up lovely Johnny there's no time to stay
   They've hoisted their topsails and hurrahed with joy
   And away o'er the ocean sailed the Lady Leroy

5. When her father found out how he cursed and did
     swear
   He sent for his captain and bid him prepare
   For to seek them and find them and their lives destroy
   For they ne'er should enjoy his proud Lady Leroy

6. The captain was pleased with his orders to go
   For to seek them and find them like some wandering
     foe
   He spied a fair vessel with her colours let fly
   He hailed her and found she was the Lady Leroy

7. He's bade them return to old Ireland once more
   Or broadside and broadside upon them would pour
   This brave Irish hero has made this reply
   We will never surrender, we'll conquer or die

8. So it's broadside and broadside each other did pour
   And louder and louder the cannons did roar
   This brave Irish hero has gained victory
   Hurrah for true lovers may they always run free

9. They've landed in Boston that city of fame
   Of the other ship's commander I'll mention no name
   Here's a health to pretty Polly long may she enjoy
   Her bravest of heroes and her Lady Leroy

From the singing of Pat Kilbride (Battlefield Band)

LEAVE HER JOHNNY

1. It's rotten meat and weevily bread
    LEAVE HER JOHNNY, LEAVE HER
    It's pump or drown the old man said
    AND IT'S TIME FOR US TO LEAVE HER

    LEAVE HER JOHNNY LEAVE HER
    OH LEAVE HER JOHNNY LEAVE HER
    FOR THE VOYAGE IS DONE
    AND THE WINDS DON'T BLOW
    AND IT'S TIME FOR US TO LEAVE HER

2. The sails are furled and the anchor stowed
    No more around Cape Horn we'll go

3. The work was hard and the wages low
    And now at last ashore we'll go

4. I thought I heard the old man say
    You can go ashore and spend your pay

From the singing of Michael Creamer

LEAVING OF LIVERPOOL

1. Farewell to you my own true love
   I am going far far away
   I am bound for California
   And I know that I'll return some day

   SO FARE THEE WELL MY OWN TRUE LOVE
   FOR WHEN I RETURN UNITED WE WILL BE
   IT'S NOT THE LEAVING OF LIVERPOOL
   THAT GRIEVES ME
   BUT MY DARLING WHEN I THINK OF THEE

2. I have shipped on a Yankee clipper ship
   Davy Crockett is her name
   And her captain's name was Burgess
   And they say she is a floating hell

3. Oh the sun is on the harbor love
   And I wish I could remain
   For I know it will be a long long time
   Before I see you again

LET THE BULGINE RUN

1. Oh the finest rig you ever could find
    AH HEE AH HO ARE YOU MOST DONE
    Is the Margaret Evans of the Black Ball Line
    CLEAR THE TRACK LET THE BULGINE RUN

    TO ME HAY RIG-A-JIG IN A JAUNTING CAR
    AH HEE AH HO ARE YOU MOST DONE
    LIZA LEE ALL ON MY KNEE
    CLEAR THE TRACK LET THE BULGINE RUN

2. In Liverpool town them girls hang 'round
    It's there me Liza can be found

3. Oh Liza Lee will you be mine
    I'll dress you up in silk so fine

4. Well the finest sight that ever you'd see
    Is Liza Lee all on my knee

5. And when I get home across the sea
    Liza will you marry me

6. I'll stay with you upon the shore
    And go away to sea no more

7. When I get back to Liverpool town
    I'll stand you whiskies all around

From the singing of Bernard Wrigley

Pocket Shantyman

LINDY LOWE

1. Come smilin' Lindy Lowe
   The prettiest gal I know

   ON THE FINEST BOAT THAT EVER FLOAT
   ON THE OHIO, THE MISSISSIPPI OR THE OHIO

2. Come smilin' Lindy Lowe
   To the Louisiana show

3. Come smilin' Lindy Lowe
   To the Gulf of Mexico

4. Come smilin' Lindy Lowe
   To the bayou deep and slow

5. Come smilin' Lindy Lowe
   Befo' that whistle blow

6. Come smilin' Lindy Lowe
   'Cause the bell done ring to go

7. Come smilin' Lindy Lowe
   Come get on board or row

From the singing of Simon Spalding

LITTLE FISHES

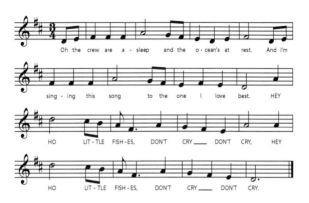

1. Oh the crew are asleep and the ocean's at rest
   And I'm singing this song to the one I love best

   HEY HO LITTLE FISHES, DON'T CRY, DON'T CRY
   HEY HO LITTLE FISHES, DON'T CRY, DON'T CRY

2. Now the ship's underway and the weather is fine
   And the skipper's down aft taking out extra line

3. Little fish when he's caught he fights like a bull whale
   That thrashes the water with his mighty tail

From the singing of Chris Coe and Bandoggs

LIVERPOOL JUDIES

1. From Liverpool to 'Frisco a-rovin' I went
   For to stay in that country was my good intent
   But drink and strong whiskey like other damn fools
   I soon got transported back to Liverpool

   SINGIN' ROW, ROW BULLIES, ROW
   THEM LIVERPOOL JUDIES HAVE GOT US IN TOW

2. A smart Yankee packet lies out in the Bay
   A-waitin' a fair wind to get under way
   With all of her sailors so sick and so sore
   They'd drunk all their whiskey and can't get no more

3. Oh here comes the mate in a hell of a stew
   He's lookin' for work for us sailors to do
   Oh it's fore tops'l halyards he loudly does roar
   And it's lay aloft Paddy ye son-o'-a-whore

4. One night off Cape Horn I shall never forget
   'Tis oft-times I sighs when I think of it yet
   She was divin' bows under with her sailors all wet
   She was doin' twelve knots with her mainskysail set

5. And now we've arrived in the Bramleymoor Dock
   And all them flash judies on the pierhead do flock
   The barrel's run dry and our five quid advance
   And I guess it's high time for to git up and dance

6. Here's a health to the Captain where'er he may be
   A bucko on land and a bully at sea
   But as for the first mate the dirty ol' brute
   We hope when he dies straight to hell he'll skyhoot

From the singing of
Nils Brown, Sean Dagher, Michiel Schrey and Clayton Kennedy
(Assassins Creed Rogue: Sea Shanty Edition)

LONDON JULIES

Ju - li - an-na, Ju-li-an-na, oh where do you go. AH HA, ME LON-DON JU - LIES. Ju - li -

an - na, Ju-li-an-na, oh where do you go. AH HA, ME LON-DON JU - LIES.

1. Julianna, Julianna, oh where do you go
   AH HA, ME LONDON JULIES
   Julianna, Julianna, oh where do you go
   AH HA, ME LONDON JULIES

2. Up aloft up aloft this yard must go
   Up aloft up aloft this yard must go

3. And around Cape Horn there's ice & snow
   But around Cape Horn we all must go

4. The mate is a bawling down below
   So heave away lash up and stow

From the singing of William Pint & Felicia Dale

LORD FRANKLIN

1. It was homeward bound one night on the deep
   Swinging in my hammock I fell asleep
   I dreamed a dream and I thought it true
   Concerning Franklin and his gallant crew

2. With one hundred seamen he sailed away
   To the frozen ocean in the month of May
   To seek a passage around the pole
   Where we poor seamen do sometimes go

3. Through cruel hardships they mainly strove
   Their ship on mountains of ice was drove
   Only the Eskimo with his skin canoe
   Was the only one that ever came through

4. In Baffin's Bay where the whale fish blow
   The fate of Franklin no man may know
   The fate of Franklin no tongue can tell
   Lord Franklin along with his sailors do dwell

5. And now my burden it gives me pain
   For my long lost Franklin I'd cross the main
   Ten thousand pounds I would freely give
   To say on earth that my Franklin do live

From the singing of John Renbourn and Pentangle

THE LOSING OF THE WHALE

(Chris Sugden)

In eight-een hun-dred and for-ty six on March the four-teenth day, I bought my-self a cal-en-dar for we were bound a-way.

1. In eighteen hundred and forty-six
   On March the fourteenth day
   I bought myself a calendar
   For we were bound away

2. We sailed from Tacky Guano
   And followed the seabird's flight
   For we were hunting whales me boys
   At least we thought we might

3. We sailed for three long days and nights
   But saw no whales at all
   The mate went up the mast to look
   While our captain went up the wall

4. We sailed for four more days and nights
   But still we had no luck
   'Til a whale come up for air me boys
   And the mate cried thar she suck

5. That whale she lashed her tail me boys
   One man on deck took a glancing blow
   But not so bad as our captain
   For he was wounded down below

6. Now the first to throw his harpoon out
   Was Valparaiso Luke
   He hit her in the tail me boys
   But they said that was a fluke

7. Now we went in with our blubber hooks
   And the whale sunk down below
   We caused her for to vomit boys
   And the mate cried thar she throw

8. Now we hauled that whale on deck me boys
   Amid many hearty cries
   But that fish it was so huge me boys
   That our vessel did capsize

9. And our captain with remorse was filled
   Likewise with water too
   I'll no more hunt the whale he cried
   If that's the last thing I don't do

10. I'll never more hunt that whale he cried
    And what's more he was right
    For the heavy seas bore down on him
    And carried him from our sight

11. And soon likewise we all were drowned
    None lived to tell the tale
    Not one of us survived to tell
    Of how we lost that whale

From the singing of the Kipper Family

LOWLANDS AWAY

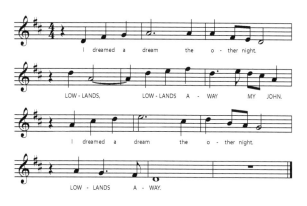

1. I dreamed a dream the other night
   LOWLANDS, LOWLANDS AWAY MY JOHN
   I dreamed a dream the other night
   LOWLANDS AWAY

2. I dreamed my love came standing by
   Came standing close to my bedside

3. He's drowning in the lowland sea
   And never more coming back to me

4. He's drowning in the lowlands low
   And never more shall I him know

5. He lies there in the windy lowlands
   He lies there in the windy lowlands

From the singing of Shirley Collins

THE LOWLANDS OF HOLLAND

1. The love that I have chosen
   I'll therewith be content
   And the salt sea shall be frozen
   Before that I repent
   Repent it shall I never
   Until the day I dee
   But the lowlands of Holland
   Have twined my love and me

2. My love lies in the salt sea
   And I am on the side
   It's enough to break a young thing's heart
   That lately was a bride
   But lately was a bonny bride
   With pleasure in her e'e
   But the lowlands of Holland
   Have twined my love and me

3. My love he built a bonny ship
   And set her on the sea
   With seven score good mariners
   To bear her company
   But there's three score of them is sunk
   And three score dead at sea
   And the lowlands of Holland
   Have twined my love and me

4. My love has built anither ship
    And set her on the sea
    And nane but twenty mariners
    All for to bring her hame
    But the weary wind began to rise
    The sea began to rout
    And my love then and his bonny ship
    Turned widdershins about

5. There shall neither quiff come on my head
    Nor comb come in my hair
    There shall neither coal nor candlelight
    Shine in my bower mair
    And neither will I marry
    Until the day I dee
    For I never had a love but one
    And he's drowned in the sea

6. Oh hold your tongue my daughter dear
    Be still and be content
    There's men enough in Galloway
    You need not sore lament
    Oh there's men enough in Galloway
    Alas there's none for me
    For I never had a love but one
    And he's drowned in the sea

From the singing of Gay Woods and Steeleye Span

MAGGIE MAY

1. Now gather round you sailor boys
    And listen to me plea
    And when you've heard me tale you'll pity me
    For I was a bloody fool
    In the port of Liverpool
    The first time that I came home from sea

    OH MAGGIE MAGGIE MAY
    THEY HAVE TAKEN HER AWAY
    SHE'LL NEVER WALK DOWN LIME STREET ANYMORE
    SHE LOVED SO MANY SAILORS
    AND CAPTAINS OF THE WHALERS
    THAT DIRTY ROBBIN' NO GOOD MAGGIE MAY

2. I was paid and just came home
   From the port of Sierra Leone
   One pound ten and fourpence was me pay
   With me pockets full of tin
   I was very soon taken in
   By a girl with the name of Maggie May

3. Oh well I do remember when
   I first met Maggie May
   She was cruising up and down Canning Place
   She'd a figure so divine
   Like a frigate of the line
   And me being just a sailor I gave chase

4. Well in the morning I awoke
   I was flat and stony broke
   No jacket, trousers, waistcoat could I find
   When I asked her where they were
   She said my very good sir
   They're down at Kelly's pawnshop number nine

5. To the pawnshop I did go
   No clothes did I find
   The policeman come and took that girl away
   Well the judge he guilty found her
   For robbin' a homeward bounder
   And paid her passage out to Botany Bay

From the singing of Dave Bullock

THE MERMAID (#1)

1. On Friday morn when we set sail
   And we were not far from the land
   When the captain he spied a mermaid so fair
   With a comb and a glass in her hand

   AND THE OCEAN WAVES WILL ROLL (WILL ROLL)
   AND STORMY WINDS WILL BLOW
   AND WE POOR SAILORS ARE SKIPPIN' AT THE TOP
   AND THE LANDLUBBERS LIE DOWN
   BELOW, BELOW, BELOW
   AND THE LANDLUBBERS LIE DOWN BELOW

2. Up spoke the captain of our gallant ship
   And a fine old man was he
   He said this fishy mermaid will warn us of the fate
   Which clings to the bottom of the sea

3. Up spoke the mate of our gallant ship
   And a brave young man was he
   Said I have a wife in Salem by the sea
   And tonight a widow she will be

4. Up spoke the cabin boy of our gallant ship
   And a fine young lad was he
   Said I have a sweetheart in Brighton by the sea
   And tonight she'll be waiting there for me

5. Up spoke the cook of our gallant ship
   And a grumpy old man was he
   Said I care much more for my pots and my pans
   Than I do for the bottom of the sea

6. Three times round spun our gallant ship
   And three times round spun she
   Three times round spun our gallant ship
   Then she sank to the bottom of the sea

From the singing of Jim Kamas

THE MERMAID (#2)

1. One night as I lay on my bed
   And lay so fast asleep
   When the thought of my true love
   Came running to my head
   And poor sailors that sail on the deep

2. As I sailed out one day one day
   And being not far from land
   There I spied a mermaid
   A-sitting on a rock
   With a comb and a glass in her hand

3. The song she sang she sang so sweet
   But no answer at all could I say
   But at length our gallant ship
   She took it round about
   Which made our poor hearts to ache

4. Then up stepped the captain of our ship
   And a well-speaking man is he
   He said I have a wife
   In fair Plymouth town
   And this night a widow she will be

5. Then up stepped the helmsman of our ship
   In his hand he held a lead and line
   For to sound the sea
   That is so wide and deep
   But no hard rock or sound could he find

6. Last night when the moon shone bright
   My mother she had some sign
   Now she may look in
   The salt salt sea
   And find but one alive

7. For a boat for a boat my fair Plymouth boys
   Don't you hear how the trumpets sound
   For the want of a longboat
   We were lost
   And most of our merry men drowned

From the singing of Lisa Moscatiello and Bob Hitchcock
(The New St. George)

THE MINGULAY BOAT SONG

HEEL YO HO, BOYS, LET HER GO, BOYS
SWING HER HEAD ROUND AND ALL TOGETHER
HEEL YO HO, BOYS, LET HER GO, BOYS
SAILING HOMEWARD TO MINGULAY

1. What care we though white the Minch is
   What care we for wind or weather
   Swing her head round, every inch is
   Sailing homeward to Mingulay

2. Wives are waiting by the quayside
   They've been waiting since break of day-o
   Swing her head round, every inch is
   Sailing homeward to Mingulay

3. When the wind is wild with shouting
   And the waves mount ever higher
   Anxious eyes turn ever seaward
   To see us home, boys, to Mingulay

MONEY DOWN

1. Your money young man is no object to me
   PAY ME THE MONEY DOWN
   Oh money down, oh money down
   PAY ME THE MONEY DOWN

2. I went for a cruise around the town
   I there met a girl called Sally Brown

3. I put my arm around her waist
   Said she young man you're in great haste

4. My price for love is half a crown
   It's half a crown or I don't drop 'em down

5. I wish I was old Stormy's son
   I'd build me a ship of ten thousand ton

6. We'd stay at the ports where we was in
   A-drinking beer and whiskey and gin

7. Now a dollar a day is a white man's pay
   For screwin' cotton all of the day

8. But the dollar a day that some has for their pay
   Would buy us rum for many a day

9. When the ship is tied up and the voyage is through
   I want my pay sir every sou

From the singing of Bernard Wrigley

MY JOHNNY WAS A SHOEMAKER

1. My Johnny was a shoemaker
   And dearly he loved me
   My Johnny was a shoemaker
   But now he's gone to sea
   With pitch and tar to soil his hands
   And to sail across the sea, stormy sea
   And sail across the stormy sea

2. His jacket was a deep sky-blue
   And curly was his hair
   His jacket was a deep sky-blue
   It was I do declare
   For to reeve the top sails up against the mast
   And to sail across the sea, stormy sea
   And sail across the stormy sea

3. Some day he'll be a captain bold
   With a brave and a gallant crew
   Some day he'll be a captain bold
   With a sword and spyglass too
   And when he has his gallant captain's sword
   He'll come home and marry me, marry me
   He'll come home and marry me

From the singing of Gay Woods and Maddy Prior
(Steeleye Span)

Pocket Shantyman

NEW YORK GIRLS

As I walked down through Chat-ham Street a fair maid I did meet.

She asked me to see her home, she lived in Bleek-er Street. AND A-

WAY YOU SAN-TY, MY DEAR HON-EY,

OH YOU NEW YORK GIRLS, CAN'T YOU DANCE THE POL-KA.

1. As I walked down through Chatham Street
   A fair maid I did meet
   She asked me to see her home
   She lived in Bleeker Street

   AND WAY YOU SANTY
   MY DEAR HONEY
   OH YOU NEW YORK GIRLS
   CAN'T YOU DANCE THE POLKA

2. And when we got to Bleeker Street
   We stopped at forty-four
   Her mother and her sister
   To meet her at the door

3. And when I got inside the house
   The drinks were passed around
   The liquor was so awful strong
   My head went round and round

4. And then we had another drink
   Before we sat to eat
   The liquor was so awful strong
   I quickly fell asleep

5. When I awoke next morning
   I had an aching head
   There was I Jack all alone
   Stark naked in my bed

6. My gold watch and my pocketbook
   And my lady friend were gone
   And there was I Jack all alone
   Stark naked in my room

7. On looking round this little room
   There's nothing I could see
   But a woman's shift and apron
   That were no use to me

8. With a flour barrel for a suit of clothes
   Down Cherry Street forlorn
   There Martin Churchill took me in
   And sent me round Cape Horn

From the singing of Tim Hart and Steeleye Span

ONE MORE DAY

1. Now's the time to leave her Johnny
   ONE MORE DAY
   And did you swear you'd not deceive her Johnny
   ONE MORE DAY
   For we're homeward bound tomorrow Johnny
   ONE MORE DAY
   And will you leave her without sorrow Johnny
   ONE MORE DAY

   ONLY ONE MORE DAY, ME JOHNNY
   ONE MORE DAY
   OH COME AND ROCK N' ROLL ME OVER
   ONE MORE DAY

2. Don't you hear the old man calling Johnny
   And don't you hear the first mate bawling Johnny
   Then put on your long-tailed blue my Johnny
   For your pay is nearly due Johnny

3. Come and row me to my lover Johnny
   And let the starlight be my cover Johnny
   Only one more day together Johnny
   No more gales nor heavy weather Johnny

From the singing of John Tams and The Home Service

OUR CAPTAIN CRIED ALL HANDS

1. Oh the captain cried all hands and away tomorrow
   Leaving my dearest dear in grief and sorrow
   Dry up your briny tears and leave off weeping
   How happy shall we be at our next meeting

2. How can you go away and fight for strangers
   You'd better stay at home here out of danger
   I'd roll you in my arms my dearest jewel
   So stay at home with me and don't be cruel

3. When I had gold in store you seemed to like me
   Now that I'm low and poor you do despise me
   You courted me a while just to deceive me
   Now my poor heart you've won and you're going to
       leave me

4. Down on the ground she fell like one a-dying
   Tearing her arms abroad, sobbing and sighing
   There's no believing men, not your own brother
   So girls if you must love, love one another

5. Farewell my dearest friends, father and mother
   I am your only child you have no other
   It's vain to weep for me for I am going
   The lad I loved so well has been my ruin

From the singing of Lisa Moscatiello and Bob Hitchcock
(The New St. George)

OUR GOOD SHIP LIES IN HARBOR

1. Our good ship lies in harbor
   Just ready to set sail
   May the heavens be your guide my love
   'Til I return again
   'TIL I RETURN AGAIN
   MAY THE HEAVENS BE YOUR GUIDE MY LOVE
   'TIL I RETURN AGAIN

2. Says the father to the daughter
   What makes you so lament
   Oh the lad that you have sent to sea
   Can give my heart content
   CAN GIVE MY HEART CONTENT
   OH THE LAD THAT YOU HAVE SENT TO SEA
   CAN GIVE MY HEART CONTENT

3. Well if that's your inclination
   The old man did reply
   I hope he will continue there
   And on the seas may die
   AND ON THE SEAS MAY DIE
   I HOPE HE WILL CONTINUE THERE
   AND ON THE SEAS MAY DIE

4. When ten long weeks were over
   And ten long tedious days
   She saw the ship come sailing in
   With her true love from the sea
   WITH HER TRUE LOVE FROM THE SEA
   SHE SAW THE SHIP COME SAILING IN
   WITH HER TRUE LOVE FROM THE SEA

5. Oh yonder stands my angel
   She's waiting there for me
   Tomorrow to the church we'll go
   And married we will be
   AND MARRIED WE WILL BE
   TOMORROW TO THE CHURCH WE'LL GO
   AND MARRIED WE WILL BE

6. Says the father to the daughter
   500 pounds I'll give
   If you'll forsake that sailor lad
   And come with me to live
   AND COME WITH ME TO LIVE
   IF YOU'LL FORSAKE THAT SAILOR LAD
   AND COME WITH ME TO LIVE

7. Well it's not your gold that glitters
   Nor your silver that do shine
   I'm going with the lad I love
   And I'm happy in my mind
   AND I'M HAPPY IN MY MIND
   I'M GOING WITH THE LAD I LOVE
   AND I'M HAPPY IN MY MIND

From the singing of Tony Engle, Danny Stradling,
Rod Stradling and Peta Webb (Oak)

Pocket Shantyman

OUTWARD AND HOMEWARD BOUND

To the Li-ver-pool docks we will bid a-dieu, to Sal and Kate and Bes-sie too. The anch-or's weighed and our sail's un-furled, we're bound to plow the wat-ery world. AND SAY WE'RE OUT-WARD BOUND, ME BOYS, HUR-RAH WE'RE OUT-WARD BOUND.

1. To the Liverpool docks we will bid adieu
   To Sal and Kate and Bessie too
   The anchor's weighed and our sail's unfurled
   We're bound to plow the watery world

   AND SAY WE'RE OUTWARD BOUND ME BOYS
   HURRAH, WE'RE OUTWARD BOUND

2. Oh the wind it blows from the east nor'east
   The ship will sail ten knots at least
   The purser will our wants supply
   And while we've grog we'll never say die

   AND SAY WE'RE OUTWARD BOUND ME BOYS…

3. And if we gets to Malabar
   Or any other port that's quite so far
   The purser then will tip the chink
   And just like fishes we will drink

   AND SAY WE'RE OUTWARD BOUND ME BOYS…

4. And when our three years they are out
   'Tis jolly near time we went about
   And when we are home and once more free
   It's won't we have a jolly spree

   AND SAY WE'RE HOMEWARD BOUND ME BOYS…

5. And when we gets to the Liverpool docks
   The pretty girls come down in flocks
   One to the other you can hear them say
   Here comes Jack with his three years' pay

   AND SAY WE'RE HOMEWARD BOUND ME BOYS…

6. And then we're off to the Bull and the Bell
   Where the best of liquors they do sell
   In comes the landlord with a smile
   Sayin' drink up lads it's worth your while

   AND SAY WE'RE HOMEWARD BOUND ME BOYS…

7. But when the money's all gone and spent
   None to be borrowed and none to be lent
   In comes the landlord with a frown
   Sayin' get up Jack let John sit down

   AND SAY WE'RE HOMEWARD BOUND ME BOYS…

8. It's then that Jack he must understand
   There's ships in port all wanting hands
   He signs on like he did before
   And bids adieu to his native shore

   AND SAY WE'RE OUTWARD BOUND ME BOYS…

From the singing of Bernard Wrigley

PADDY LAY BACK

1. Once there was a great demand for sailors
FOR SAILORS
For the Colonies for Frisco and for France
AND FOR FRANCE
So I shipped aboard a limey bark the Hotspur
THE HOTSPUR
Got paralytic drunk on my advance
MY ADVANCE

Paddy lay back PADDY LAY BACK
Take in the slack TAKE IN THE SLACK
Take a turn around the capstan heave a pawl
HEAVE A PAWL
About ship's station boys be handy BE HANDY
WE'RE BOUND FOR VALAPARAISO ROUND THE HORN

2. 'Twas on the quarter deck that I first saw 'em
   Such an ugly bunch you'd never seen before
   For the skipper had shipped a shanghaied crew of
      Dutchmen
   It made me poor old heart feel sick and sore

3. Now some of the other sailors had been drinking
   I myself was heavy on the booze
   So I sat down on me old sea chest a-thinkin'
   To turn into me bunk and take a snooze

4. Well I asked the mate to which a watch was mine-o
   Says he I'll tell you which a watch is which
   He blew me down he kicked me hard astern-o
   Calling me a dirty lousy son of a gun (BITCH BITCH)

5. I quickly made my mind up I should leave her
   Leave the bugger and get a job ashore
   I swam across the bay I went and left her
   And in an English bar I found a whore (HAR HAR)

From the singing of Charles O'Hegarty and The Starboard List

PADDY WEST

1. Oh as I was a-walkin' down London Road
   I come to Paddy West's house
   He gave me a feed of American hash
   And he called it Liverpool scouse
   He said there's a ship that's wantin' hands
   And on her you quickly sign
   The mate is a bastard, the bosun's worse
   But she will suit you fine

   TAKE OFF YOUR DUNGAREE JACKETS
   AND GIVE YOURSELVES A REST
   AND WE'LL THINK ON THEM COLD NOR'WESTERS
   THAT WE HAD AT PADDY WEST'S

2. Well when I'd had a feed my boys
   The wind began to blow
   He sent me up in the attic
   The main-royal for to stow
   But when I got up in the attic
   No main-royal could I find
   So I turned around to the window
   And I furled the window blind

3. Now Paddy he piped all hands on deck
   Their stations for to man
   His wife stood in the doorway
   With a bucket in her hand
   And Paddy sings out now let 'er rip
   And she flung the water our way
   Sayin' clew up your fore t'gan'sl, boys
   She's takin' in the spray

4. Now seein' we're off to the south'ard, boys
   To Frisco we was bound
   Old Paddy he called for a length of rope
   And he laid it on the ground
   And we all stepped over and back again
   And he says to me that's fine
   Now when they ask if you've been to sea
   You can say you've crossed the line

5. Now there's only one thing for you to do
   Before you sail away
   That's to step around the table
   Where the bullock's horn do lay
   And when they ask you were you ever at sea
   You can say ten times 'round the Horn
   And Bejesus you're a sailor since
   The day that you was born

Final chorus:
PUT ON YOUR DUNGAREE JACKET
AND WALK OUT LOOKIN' YOUR BEST
AND TELL 'EM YOU'RE AN OLD SAILOR MAN
THAT'S COME FROM PADDY WEST'S

*From the singing of A.L. Lloyd
and Louis Killen*

PAY ME MY MONEY DOWN

PAY ME, PAY ME
PAY ME MY MONEY DOWN
PAY ME OR YOU GOES TO JAIL
PAY ME MY MONEY DOWN

1. You pay me, you owe me
   PAY ME MY MONEY DOWN
   Pay me Mr. Steviedore
   PAY ME MY MONEY DOWN

2. If I had a-known the boss was blind
   I woulda went to work at half past nine

3. I thought I heard the captain say
   Tomorrow will be your sailing day

4. If I was Mr. Alfred Jones' son
   I'd stay in the house and drink good rum

5. I heard them talking in the deck below
   If you don't pay me this ship won't go

PLEASANT AND DELIGHTFUL

1. It was pleasant and delightful
   On one Midsummer's morn
   And the green fields and the meadows
   They were buried in corn
   And the blackbirds and thrushes
   Sang on every green tree
   And the larks they sang melodious
   At the dawning of the day
   AND THE LARKS THEY SANG MELODIOUS
   AND THE LARKS THEY SANG MELODIOUS
   AND THE LARKS THEY SANG MELODIOUS
   AT THE DAWNING OF THE DAY

2. A sailor and his true love
   Were a-walking one day
   Said the sailor to his true love
   I am bound far away
   I am bound for the East Indies
   Where the loud cannons roar
   And I'm going to leave my Nancy
   She's the girl that I adore
   AND I'M GOING TO LEAVE MY NANCY…ETC.

3. Said the sailor to his true love
   Well I must be on my way
   For our topsails they are hoisted
   And our anchors are weighed
   Our big ship she lies waiting
   For the next flowing tide
   And if ever I return again
   I will make you my bride
   AND IF EVER I RETURN AGAIN…etc.

4. Then a ring from offen her finger
   She instantly drew
   Saying take this dearest William
   And me heart will go too
   And as he embraced her
   Tears from her eyes fell
   Saying may I go along with you
   Oh no my love farewell
   SAYING MAY I GO ALONG WITH YOU…etc.

From the singing of Louis Killen

POOR OLD HORSE

1. They say old man your horse will die
   AND THEY SAY SO, AND WE HOPE SO
   They say old man your horse will die
   OH POOR OLD MAN

2. And if he dies then we'll tan his hide
   And if he dies then we'll tan his hide

3. And if he lives then we'll ride again
   And if he lives then we'll ride again

4. And it's after years of much abuse
   Then we'll salt him down for the sailors' use

5. He's as dead as a nail in the lamp room floor
   He's as dead as a nail in the lamp room floor

6. Aye and he won't bother us no more
   Aye and he won't bother us no more

7. And it's Sally's in the garden and she's pickin' the peas
   And her long black hair's hangin' down to her knees

8. And it's Sally's in the kitchen and she's baking the duff
   And the cheeks of her arse are going chuff chuff chuff

9. And it's down the long and the winding road
   And it's down the long and the winding road

10. It's mahogany beef and the weevily bread
    It's mahogany beef and the weevily bread

11. And I thought I heard the old man say
    Just one more pull and then belay

12. Just one more pull and that will do
    For we're the lads to kick her through

From the singing of John Tams and The Albion Band

PRETTY NANCY OF YARMOUTH

1. Pretty Nancy of Yarmouth
   She's my own heart's delight
   And a long and kind letter
   Unto her I did write
   All for to inform her
   What we had to undergo
   While sailin' on the ocean
   Where stormy winds blow

2. On the 18th of October
   Our bark it set sail
   Pretty Nancy come down
   For to bid me farewell
   She said while you're sailing
   On the wide waste of blue
   She said my young sailor
   I'll be faithful to you

3. Long years then did pass
   When back I did return
   Pretty Nancy was married
   Had a home of her own
   While I was a-sailing
   On the wide restless sea
   Pretty Nancy proved faithless
   And false unto me

4. So come all you young sailors
   And listen to me
   And never leave the lass you love
   For to plow the salt sea
   For while you are sailing
   On the wide ocean blue
   She'll prove faithless
   Like Nancy of Yarmouth to you

From the singing of Peter Bellamy, Royston Wood and Heather Wood (The Young Tradition)

THE RAMBLING SAILOR

1. I am a sailor brisk and bold
    That oft have sailed the ocean
    I've travelled the country far and near
    For honour and promotion
    Me shipmates all I'll bid you adieu
    I may no longer go along with you
    I'll travel the country through and through
    And they call me the rambling sailor

2. And if you want to know my name
    My name it is Young Johnson
    I've got a commission from the King
    To court all girls as handsome
    With my false heart and flattering tongue
    I'll court them all both old and young
    I'll court them all but I marry none
    And they call me the rambling sailor

3. Well first I come to Plymouth town
   And there were lasses many
   I boldly stepped unto a one
   To court her for her money
   Says I me dear be of good cheer
   I will not leave you do not fear
   I'll travel the country far and near
   And they call me the rambling sailor

4. And next I come to Portsmouth town
   And there was lasses plenty
   I boldly stepped unto a one
   To court her for her beauty
   Says I me dear what do you choose
   Here's ale and a wine and a rum punch too
   Besides a pair of silks and shoes
   If you travel with the rambling sailor

5. And then I rose up with the dawn
   Just as the day was peeping
   On tiptoe down the stairs I went
   And I left my love a-sleeping
   And if she waits until I come
   She may lie there 'til the day of her doom
   I'll court some other girl in the room
   And they call me the rambling sailor

From the singing of Tim Hart

RANDY DANDY-O

1. Now we are ready
   To sail for the Horn
   WAY HEY ROLL AND GO
   Our boots and our clothes boys
   Are all in the pawn
   TO ME ROLLICKING RANDY DANDY-O

   HEAVE A PAWL
   NOW HEAVE AWAY
   WAY HEY ROLL AND GO
   THE ANCHOR'S ON BOARD
   AND THE CABLE'S ALL STORED
   TO ME ROLLICKING RANDY DANDY-O

2. Soon we'll be warping her
   Out through the locks
   Where them pretty young girls
   All come down in their frocks

3. Come breast the bar bullies
   And heave her away
   Soon we'll be rolling her
   Down through the bay

4. So it's goodbye to Sally
   And goodbye to Sue
   For we are the bullies
   That can kick her through

5. Roust her up bullies
   The wind's drawing free
   Let's get the glad-rags on
   And drive her to sea

6. It's up them yards
   You parish-rigged bums
   Get your hands out your pockets
   And don't suck your thumbs

7. We're outward bound
   For Valipo Bay
   Get bending me boys
   'Tis a hell of a way

RANT & ROAR (SPANISH LADIES)

1. Farewell and adieu
   You gay Spanish ladies
   Farewell and adieu
   You ladies of Spain
   For we've received orders
   To sail for old England
   But we hope in a short time
   To see you again

WE'LL RANT AND WE'LL ROAR
LIKE TRUE-BRITISH SAILORS
WE'LL RANT AND WE'LL ROAR
ALL ACROSS THE SALT SEA
UNTIL WE STRIKE SOUNDINGS
IN THE CHANNEL OF OLD ENGLAND
FROM USHANT TO SCILLY
IS THIRTY-FIVE LEAGUES

2. So we hove our ship to
   With the wind at sou'westward
   We hove our ship to
   Our soundings for to see
   We rounded and sounded
   And we got forty-five fathoms
   We squared our main yard
   And up channel steered we

3. Well the first land we made
   It was called the Dunman
   Then Ringhead off Plymouth
   Off Portland and Wight
   We passed by Beachy
   By Fairly and Dungeness
   Then we hove our ship to
   In the South Foreland Light

4. Then the signal was made
   For the grand fleet to anchor
   All in the Downs
   That night for to meet
   And it's stand by your stoppers
   Let go your shank-painters
   Haul all your clew garnets
   Get out tacks and sheets

5. Now let every man
   Toss off a full bumper
   And let every man
   Toss off a full bowl
   We'll drink and be jolly
   And drown melancholy
   Sayin' here's a good health
   To all stout-hearted souls

From the singing of Bob Kotta (Howling Gael)

REUBEN RANZO

1. Oh poor old Reuben Ranzo
   RANZO ME BOYS, RANZO
   Oh poor old Reuben Ranzo
   RANZO ME BOYS, RANZO

2. Ranzo was no sailor
   But he shipped onboard a whaler

3. Oh they gave him lashes thirty
   Because he was so dirty

4. The captain had a daughter
   She gave him more than she oughter

5. She gave him an education
   She taught him navigation

6. Now Ranzo was a sailor
   He's captain of a whaler

7. Now he's known where all the whalefish blow
   The hardest bastard on the go

From the singing of Dave Burland and Hedgehog Pie

RIO GRANDE

1. I'll sing you a song a good song of the sea
AWAY RIO
I'll sing you a song if you'll sing it with me
AND WE'RE BOUND FOR THE RIO GRANDE

   AND IT'S AWAY RIO, AWAY RIO
IT'S FARE YOU WELL MY PRETTY YOUNG GIRLS
AND WE'RE BOUND FOR THE RIO GRANDE

2. We'll man the good capstan and run her around
We'll haul up the anchor to this jolly sound

3. The anchors are weighed and the sails are all set
The girls that we're leaving we'll never forget

4. It's goodbye to Sally and goodbye to Sue
And to them thats is listening it's farewell to you

*From the singing of John "Fud" Benson, Jeff Warner,
Gerret Warner, Louis Killen*

ROLL ALABAMA ROLL

(Frank Townsend, 1864)

1. When the Alabama's keel was laid
   ROLL ALABAMA ROLL
   It was laid in the yard of Jonathan Laird
   OH ROLL ALABAMA ROLL

2. She was laid in the yard of Jonathan Laird
   It was in the town of Birkenhead

3. On the Mersey way she sailed then
   She was Liverpool fitted with guns and men

4. To the Western Islands she sailed forth
   To destroy the commerce of the North

5. To Cherbourg port she went one day
   To take a share of prize money

6. Oh many a sailor met his doom
   When the Kearsarge she hove in to view

7. A shot from the forward pivot that day
   Shot the Alabama's keel away

8. Off the three mile limit in '64
   The Alabama sank to the ocean floor

From the singing of Bill Staines

ROLL DOWN

(Peter Bellamy)

1. Sweet ladies of Plymouth
   We're saying goodbye
   ROLL DOWN
   We'll rock you and roll you
   Again by and by
   WALK AROUND ME BRAVE BOYS AND ROLL DOWN

   AND WE WILL ROLL DOWN
   WALK AROUND ME BRAVE BOYS AND ROLL DOWN

2. Now the anchor's aweigh
   And the sails are unfurled
   We're bound for to take her
   Half way round the world

3. In the wide Bay of Biscay
   The seas do run high
   Those poor sickly transports
   They'll wish they could die

4. When the wild coast of Africa
   It do appear
   Those poor nervous transports
   They'll tremble with fear

5. When the Cape of Good Hope
   It is rounded at last
   Those poor lonesome transports
   They'll long for the past

6. When the great southern whales
   Off our quarter do spout
   Those poor simple transports
   They'll goggle and shout

7. And when we arrive
   On Australia's strand
   The poor weary transports
   They'll long for the land

8. And when we set sail
   For old England's shore
   The poor stranded transports
   We'll see them no more

9. Then sweet ladies of Plymouth
   We'll pay all your rent
   We'll go sailing no more
   'Til our money's all spent

From the singing of Cyril Tawney

ROLL THE OLD CHARIOT ALONG

1. Well a nice drop of beer wouldn't do us any harm
   Yes a nice drop of beer wouldn't do us any harm
   A nice drop of beer wouldn't do us any harm
   And we'll all hang on behind

   AND WE'LL ROLL THE OLD CHARIOT ALONG
   WE'LL ROLL THE OLD CHARIOT ALONG
   WE'LL ROLL THE OLD CHARIOT ALONG
   AND WE'LL ALL HANG ON BEHIND

2. And a nice jug of punch…

3. And a plate of Irish stew…

4. And a nice plum duff…

5. And a night on the town…

6. And a night with the girls…

From the singing of Michael Creamer

ROLL THE WOODPILE DOWN

Way down South where the cocks do crow. WAY DOWN IN FLO-RI-DA. Them girls all dance to the old ban-jo. AND WE'LL ROLL THE WOOD-PILE DOWN. ROL-LIN' ROL-LIN' ROL-LIN' THE WHOLE WORLD ROUND. THAT BROWN GAL O' MINE'S DOWN THE GEOR-GIA LINE AND WE'LL ROLL THE WOOD-PILE DOWN.

1. Way down South where the cocks do crow
   WAY DOWN IN FLORIDA
   Them girls all dance to the old banjo
   AND WE'LL ROLL THE WOODPILE DOWN

   ROLLIN', ROLLIN'
   ROLLIN' THE WHOLE WORLD ROUND
   THAT BROWN GAL O' MINE'S
   DOWN THE GEORGIA LINE
   AND WE'LL ROLL THE WOODPILE DOWN

2. When I was a young man in my prime
   I chased them yeller gals two at a time

3. We'll roll him high and we'll roll him low
   We'll heave him up and away we'll go

4. Oh rouse and bust her is the cry
   A black man's wage is never high

5. Oh Curly goes on the old ran tan
   Oh Curly's just a down east man

6. Oh one more heave and that will do
   We're the bullies for to kick her through

ROLLING DOWN TO OLD MAUI

1. It's a damned hard life full of toil and strife
   We whalermen undergo
   And we don't give a damn when the gales is done
   How hard the wind did blow
   For we're homeward bound 'tis a grand old sound
   With a good ship taut and free
   And we don't give a damn as we drink our rum
   Rolling down to old Maui

   ROLLING DOWN TO OLD MAUI, ME BOYS
   ROLLING DOWN TO OLD MAUI
   WE'RE HOMEWARD BOUND
   FROM THE ARCTIC GROUND
   ROLLING DOWN TO OLD MAUI

2. And now we sail with a northerly gale
   Through the ice and the wind and the rain
   The coconut fronds them tropical lands
   We soon shall see again
   Six hellish months we've passed away
   In the cold Kamchatka sea
   But we're homeward bound from the arctic ground
   Rolling down to old Maui

3. Once more we sail with a northerly gale
   Towards our island home
   Our mainmast sprung but our whaling's done
   We ain't got far to roam
   And our stunsail boom is carried away
   What care we for that sound
   A living gale is after us
   Thank God we're homeward bound

4. How soft the breeze through the island trees
   Now the ice is far astern
   Them native maids in them island glades
   Are awaiting our return
   Even now their big brown eyes look out
   Hoping some fine day to see
   Our baggy sails running 'fore the gales
   Rolling down to old Maui

From the singing of Bill Price

THE ROSABELLA

One Monday morning in the month of May, a Monday morning in the month of May. I thought I heard the old man say, the Ro - sa - bel - la sails to - day. WE'RE GOING ON BOARD THE RO-SA - BEL-LA, WE ARE GOING ON BOARD THE RO-SA - BEL-LA, WE ARE GOING ON BOARD RIGHT DOWN TO BOARD THE SAU - CY RO - SA - BEL-LA.

1. One Monday morning in the month of May
   A Monday morning in the month of May
   I thought I heard the old man say
   The Rosabella sails today

   WE'RE GOING ON BOARD THE ROSABELLA
   WE ARE GOING ON BOARD THE ROSABELLA
   WE ARE GOING ON BOARD RIGHT DOWN TO BOARD
   THE SAUCY ROSABELLA

2. She's a deepwater ship with a deepwater crew
   She's a deepwater ship with a deepwater crew
   We can stick by the coast but we're damned if we do
   Aboard the Rosabella

3. Them Bowery girls they make me grieve
   Them Bowery girls they make me grieve
   They took my money and they make me leave
   Aboard the Rosabella

4. Around Cape Horn in the month of May
   Around Cape Horn in the month of May
   Around Cape Horn is a damned long way
   Aboard the Rosabella

*From the singing of Richard Fewtrell, Dick Holdstock and
Alan MacLeod*

ROUND THE BAY OF MEXICO

1. Round the Bay of Mexico
   WAY OH SUZIANNA
   Mexico's the place that I belong in
   ROUND THE BAY OF MEXICO

2. Been to sea for a month or more
   Looking forward to my time on shore

3. The wind is high, the sky is blue
   Bound to anchor in a day or two

4. I can see it all before my eye
   A big café and bottle full of rye

5. Some beans and rice to soothe my taste
   I ain't gonna let nothin' go to waste

6. Put some kerchiefs in my bag
   Tell a tale or two so I can really brag

7. There's Rosita and Chiquita and pretty maid Belle
   If I meet 'em all at once I'll never get well

From the singing of Harry Belafonte

ROUNDING OF CAPE HORN

1. The gallant frigate Amphitrite
   She lay in Plymouth Sound
   Blue Peter at the foremast head
   For she was outward bound
   We was waiting there for orders
   To send us far from home
   The orders came for Rio
   And thence around Cape Horn

2. When we arrived at Rio
   We prepared for heavy gales
   We bent on all the rigging boys
   Bent on all new sails
   From ship to ship they cheered us
   As we did sail along
   And wished us pleasant weather
   In the rounding of Cape Horn

3. While beating off Magellan Straits
    It blew exceeding hard
    When shortening sail two gallant tars
    Fell from the topsail yard
    By angry seas the ropes we threw
    From their poor hands was torn
    We was forced to leave them to the sharks
    That prowl around Cape Horn

4. When we got round the Horn, me boys
    We had some glorious days
    And very soon our killick dropped
    In Valparaiso Bay
    Them pretty girls came down in flocks
    I solemnly declare
    They're far before those Plymouth girls
    With their long and curly hair

5. They love a jolly sailor
    When he spends his money free
    They'll laugh and sing and merry merry be
    And have a jovial spree
    And when your money is all gone
    They'll not on you impose
    They are not like those Plymouth girls
    That'll pawn and sell your clothes

6. Farewell to Valparaiso
    And farewell for a while
    Likewise to all the Spanish girls
    Along the coast of Chile
    And if ever I live to be paid off
    I'll sit and sing this song
    God bless those pretty Spanish girls
    We left around Cape Horn

From the singing of Tony Hall

SALLY RACKET

1. Little Sally Racket
    HAUL HIM AWAY
    She pawned my best jacket
    HAUL HIM AWAY
    And she lost the ticket
    HAUL HIM AWAY
    And a hauley high-o
    HAUL HIM AWAY

2. Little Kitty Carson
    Got off with the parson
    Now she's got a little barson
    And a hauley high-o

3. Well a little Nancy Dawson
    Well she got a notion
    For a poor old bosun
    And a hauley high-o

4. Little Suzie Skinner
    She said she's a beginner
    And she prefers it to her dinner
    Serve up lads and win her

5. Well me fightin' cocks now
   All and split her blocks now
   And we'll stretch her luff boys
   And that'll be enough boys

From the singing of A.L. Lloyd

SAM'S GONE AWAY

1. I wish I was a cabin boy aboard a man-o'-war

   SAM'S GONE AWAY, ABOARD A MAN-O'-WAR
   PRETTY WORK BRAVE BOYS
   PRETTY WORK I SAY
   SAM'S GONE AWAY, ABOARD A MAN-O'-WAR
   SAM'S GONE AWAY, ABOARD A MAN-O'-WAR

2. I wish I was a gunner aboard a man-o'-war

3. I wish I was a bosun aboard a man-o'-war

4. I wish I was a purser aboard a man-o'-war

5. I wish I was a captain aboard a man-o'-war

6. I wish I was an admiral aboard a man-o'-war

7. I wish I was a shantyman aboard a man-o'-war

From the singing of Caryl P. Weiss

SANTIANO

1. Oh Santiano gained the day
   HOORAY SANTIANO
   Oh Santiano gained the day
   ALL ALONG THE PLAINS OF MEXICO

2. Oh Mexico, oh Mexico
   Oh Mexico where I must got

3. When I was a young man in my prime
   I knocked them little girls two at a time

4. Oh why do them yellow gals love me so
   Because I don't tell 'em all I know

5. Them Liverpool gals ain't got no combs
   They comb their hair with a kipper backbone

6. Oh times is hard and the wages low
   And it's time for us to roll and go

From the singing of Russell Fory, Evelyne Taylor, Tim Taylor and Gary Young (The Banded Geckos)

SAUCY SAILOR

Come my own one, come my fair one, come now un-to me. Could you fan-cy a poor sai-lor lad who has just come from sea.

1. Come my own one, come my fair one
   Come now unto me
   Could you fancy a poor sailor lad
   Who has just come from sea

2. You are ragged love, you are dirty love
   And your clothes smell much of tar
   So be gone you saucy sailor lad
   So be gone you Jack Tar

3. If I am ragged love and I am dirty love
   And my clothes smell much of tar
   I have silver in my pocket love
   And gold in great store

4. And then when she heard him say so
   On her bended knees she fell
   I will marry my dear Henry
   For I love a sailor lad so well

5. Do you think that I am foolish love
   Do you think that I am mad
   For to wed with a poor country girl
   Where no fortune's to be had

6. I will cross the briny ocean
   I will whistle and sing
   And since you have refused the offer love
   Some other girl shall wear the ring

7. I am frolicsome, I am easy
   Good tempered and free
   And I don't give a single pin my boys
   What the world thinks of me

From the singing of Maddy Prior and Steeleye Span

SHALLOW BROWN

1. Oh I'm going to leave her
   SHALLOW, OH SHALLOW BROWN
   Oh I'm going to leave her
   SHALLOW BROWN, SHALLOW BROWN

2. Ship on board of a whaler
   Ship on board a whaler

3. Bound away for St. Georges
   Bound away for St. Georges

4. Love thee well Juliana
   Love thee well Juliana

5. Master's going to sell me
   Master's going to sell me

6. Sell me to the Yankees
   Sell me to the Yankees

7. Sell me for the dollar
   Great big Spanish dollar

8. Oh I'm going to leave her
   Oh I'm going to leave her

From the singing of Tony Hall

SHIP IN DISTRESS

You sea-men bold who plough the o-cean see dan-gers lands-men nev-er know. 'Tis nor for hon - or or pro-mo-tion, no tongue can tell what they un-der-go. In the blust-er-ous wind and the great dark wa - ter our ship went drift-ing on the sea. Her rig-ging gone and her rud-der bro-ken which brought us to ex - trem - i - ty.

1. You seamen bold who plough the ocean
   See dangers landsmen never know
   'Tis not for honour or promotion
   No tongue can tell what they undergo
   In the blusterous wind and the great dark water
   Our ship went drifting on the sea
   Her rigging gone and her rudder broken
   Which brought us to extremity

2. For fourteen days heartsore and hungry
   Seeing but wild water and bitter sky
   Poor fellows all stood in a totter
   A-casting lots as to who should die
   Their lot it fell on Robert Jackson
   Whose family was so great
   I'm free to die but oh me comrades
   Let me keep look-out 'til the break of day

3. A full dressed ship like the sun a-glittering
   Came bearing down to their relief
   As soon as this glad news was shouted
   It banished all their care and grief
   Our ship brought to, no longer drifting
   Safe in Saint Vincent, Cape Verde she lay
   You seamen all who hear my story
   Pray you'll ne'er suffer the like again

From the singing of Louis Killen

Pocket Shantyman

SOUTH AUSTRALIA

1. In South Australia I was born
   HEAVE AWAY, HAUL AWAY
   In South Australia round Cape Horn
   WE'RE BOUND FOR SOUTH AUSTRALIA

   HAUL AWAY YOU ROLLING KING
   HEAVE AWAY, HAUL AWAY
   HAUL AWAY YOU'LL HEAR ME SING
   WE'RE BOUND FOR SOUTH AUSTRALIA

2. Oh South Australia's a decent place
   To get drunk there is no disgrace

3. Oh South Australia's a decent land
   Full of lizards, flies and sand

4. As I went out one morning fair
   It's there I met Miss Nancy Blair

5. I shook her up I shook her down
   I shook her round and round the town

6. There ain't but one thing grieves me mind
   To leave Miss Nancy Blair behind
   From the singing of The Starboard List

STATELY SOUTHERNER

She was a state-ly South-ern-er that flew the Stars and Bars. The
whist-ling wind from the west north-west blew through her pitch pine spars. As
like an ea-gle swift-ly on she flew be-fore the gale. 'Til
late that night she raised a-live the Old Head of Kin-sale.

1. She was a stately Southerner
   That flew the Stars and Bars
   The whistling wind from the west northwest
   Blew through her pitch-pine spars
   As like an eagle swiftly on
   She flew before the gale
   'Til late that night she raised alive
   The Old Head of Kinsale

2. No thought was there of shortening sail
   By him who trod the poop
   Though by the weight of the ponderous jibs
   The boom bent like a hoop
   Our groaning chesstrees told the strain
   That bore the stout main tack
   But he only laughed as he gazed abaft
   At the bright and silvery track

3. It was a fine and a cloudless night
   The breeze held steady and strong
   As gaily o'er the shining deep
   Our good ship bowled along
   In foam beneath the trembling bows
   A-mounting waves she spread
   As stooping low her breast of snow
   She buried her lee cat-head

4. What looms upon the starboard bow
   What hangs upon the breeze
   'Tis time the package hauls her wind
   Abreast the old Saltee
   For by a mighty press of sails
   That clothed each ponderous spar
   That ship we spied on the misty tide
   Was a British man-o'-war

5. Out booms, out booms our skipper cried
   Out booms and give her sheet
   And the swiftest ship that ever was launched
   Shot away from the British fleet
   Amidst a murderous hail of shots
   And stun'sails hoisted away
   Down channel clear Paul Jones did steer
   Just at the break of day

From the singing of Tim Hart and Maddy Prior

STRIKE THE BELL

1. Out on the quarter deck
    And walking about
    There's the second mate
    So steady and so stout
    What he is a-thinkin' of
    He doesn't know himself
    We wish that he would hurry up and
    Strike, strike the bell

STRIKE THE BELL, SECOND MATE
LET US GO BELOW
LOOK A-WELL TO WINDWARD
YOU CAN SEE IT'S GOING TO BLOW
LOOK AT THE GLASS
YOU CAN SEE THAT IT HAS FELL
WE WISH THAT YOU WOULD HURRY UP AND
STRIKE, STRIKE THE BELL

2. Down on the main deck
A-workin' on the pumps
There's the starboard watch
A-longin' for their bunks
Look out to windward
And see a great swell
We wish that he would hurry up and
Strike, strike the bell

3. Aft at the wheel
Poor Anderson stands
Grasping at the spokes
With his cold mittened hands
Looks at the compass
And the course is clear as hell
We wish that he would hurry up and
Strike, strike the bell

4. Forward at the fo'c'slehead
And keeping sharp lookout
Yonder Johnny's standing
Ready for to shout
Lights are burning bright sir
And everything is well
We wish that he would hurry up and
Strike, strike the bell

5. Out on the poop deck
   The gallant captain stands
   Looking out to sea
   With a spyglass in his hands
   What he is a-thinkin' of
   We know very well
   He's thinking more of shortening sail
   Than striking the bell

*From the singing of John "Fud" Benson, Jeff Warner,
Gerret Warner, Louis Killen*

TALCAHUANO GIRLS

1. I've been a ship's cook and I've been a clipperman
   I can dance I can sing I can walk the jib boom
   I can handle a harpoon and cut a fine figure
   Whenever I get in a boat's standing room

   WE'LL RANT AND WE'LL ROAR
   LIKE TRUEBORN YOUNG WHALERMEN
   WE'LL RANT AND WE'LL ROAR ON DECK OR BELOW
   UNTIL WE SEE BOTTOM INSIDE THE TWO SINKERS
   THEN STRAIGHT UP THE CHANNEL
   TO HUASCO WE'LL GO

2. I was in Talcahuano last year in a whaler
   I bought some gold broaches for the girls in the Bay
   I bought me a clay pipe they called it a Meerschaum
   It melted like butter on a hot sunny day

3. I went to a dance one night in old Tumbez
   There was plenty of talent as much as you'd wish
   There was one little girl there a-chewing tobacco
   Just like a young kitten a-chewing fresh fish

4. Farewell to the girls of old Talcahuano
   Farewell to the girls of far-off Maui
   Let's drink and be merry don't be melancholy
   I can't marry youse all or in chokey I'd be

From the singing of Robin & Barry Dransfield

TOMMY'S GONE AWAY

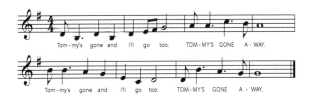

1. Tommy's gone and I'll go too
   TOMMY'S GONE AWAY
   Tommy's gone and I'll go too
   TOMMY'S GONE AWAY

2. Tommy's gone to Callao
   He won't come back to me you know

3. Tommy's gone to Vallipo
   He'll dance them Spanish girls you know

4. Tommy's gone to far Quebec
   He's stowin' timber on the deck

5. Tommy's gone to Montreal
   In a packet ship with skysails tall

6. And Tommy's gone to Rio Grande
   He's rollin' in the yellow sand

7. Tommy's gone to Singapore
   He'll dance upon that sunny shore

8. And Tommy's gone to Frisco Bay
   Around Cape Horn the other day

9. Tommy's gone to Cardiff town
   Where the girls all come on down

10. And Tommy's gone to Swansea Bay
    See the girls all shout hooray

11. Tommy's gone to Harvard west
    They'll give Tommy all their best

12. And Tommy's gone to Abergwaun
    That's Sheila haulin' on the line

13. Tommy's gone forever more
    Tommy's gone forever more

From the singing of Mick Tems (Calennig)

Pocket Shantyman

TOM'S GONE TO HILO

1. Tommy's gone on a whaling ship
   AWAY TO HILO
   Oh Tommy's gone on a damn long trip
   TOM'S GONE TO HILO

2. He never kissed his girl goodbye
   He left her and he told her why

3. She robbed him blind and left him broke
   He had enough, gave her the poke

4. His half-pay went, it went like chaff
   She hung around for the other half

5. She drank and boozed his pay away
   With her weather-eye on his next pay day

6. Oh Tommy's gone and left her flat
   Oh Tommy's gone and he won't come back

From the singing of John Bentley

THE TURK-DUFFING SONG

1. On the 25th of February
   The weather being clear
   We spied seven ships of Turkish men-of-war
   All belonging to Algiers

   TO ME RIGHT FOL LETTER-O, RIGHT FOL LETTER-O
   RIGHT FOL LETTER-OL DAY
   RATTLE DIDDLE DI, RATTLE DIDDLE DI
   TO ME RIGHT FOL LETTER-OL DAY

2. Well the first ship that we came up to
   It was the Pink so clear
   Commanded by a big black dog
   And belonging to Algiers

3. Well the next ship that we came upon
   It was the Rose and Crown
   We fired a big broadside at her
   And quickly she went down

4. Well the very next ship we came alongside
   It was the Harp and Lyre
   We tossed our pitchpoles into her
   And quickly she caught fire

5. Well three we sunk and two they ran
   And two we carried away
   We brought them back to England's shore
   To show we'd won the day

From the singing of Dave Rowan

WAITIN' FOR THE DAY

The worst old ship that ev-er did weigh, sailed out of Har-wich on a win-dy day. AND WE'RE

WAIT-IN' FOR THE DAY, WAIT-IN' FOR THE DAY, WAIT-IN' FOR THE DAY THAT WE GET OUR PAY.

1. The worst old ship that ever did weigh
   Sailed out of Harwich on a windy day

   AND WE'RE WAITIN' FOR THE DAY
   WAITIN' FOR THE DAY
   WAITIN' FOR THE DAY
   THAT WE GET OUR PAY

2. She was built in Roman time
   Held together with bits of twine

3. The skipper's half drunk and the mate is too
   And the crew is fourteen men too few

4. Nothing in the galley, nothing in the hold
   But the skipper's turned in with a bag of gold

5. Off Orford Ness she sprang a leak
   Hear her poor old timbers creak

6. Through the Cockle to Cromer cliff
   Steering like a wagon with a wheel adrift

7. Into the Humber and up the town
   Pump you blighters, pump or drown

8. Her coal was shot by a Keadby crew
   Her bottom was rotten and it went right through

From the singing of Bob Roberts

THE WATER IS WIDE

1. The water is wide I cannot cross o'er
   And neither have I wings to fly
   Give me a boat that can carry two
   And both shall row my love and I

2. A ship there is and she sails the sea
   She's loaded deep as deep can be
   But not so deep as this love I'm in
   I know not how I sink or swim

3. I leaned my back against an oak
   Thinking it was a trusty tree
   But first it bent and then it broke
   And thus did my false love to me

4. Love is gentle and love is kind
   The sweetest flower when first it is new
   But love grows old and waxes cold
   And fades away like the summer's dew

5. The water is wide I cannot cross o'er
   And neither have I wings to fly
   Give me a boat that can carry two
   And both shall row my love and I

From the singing of John McCutcheon

THE WEARY CUTTERS

1. Oh the weary cutters and oh the weary sea
    Oh the weary cutters have taken my laddie from me
    They've pressed him far away foreign
    With Nelson beyond the salt sea

2. Oh the lousy cutters and oh the weary sea
    Oh the lousy cutters have stolen my laddie from me
    They always come in the night
    They never come in the day
    They come at night and steal the laddies away

3. Oh the weary cutters and oh the weary sea
    Oh the weary cutters have taken my laddie from me
    I'll give the cutter a guinea
    I'll give the cutter no more
    I'll give him a guinea to steal my laddie ashore

From the singing of Maddy Prior

WEARY WHALING GROUNDS

1. If I had the wings of a gull me boys
   I would spread 'em and fly home
   I'd leave old Greenland's icy grounds
   For of right whales there is none
   And the weather's rough and the winds do blow
   And there's little comfort here
   I'd sooner be snug in a Deptford pub
   A-drinkin' of strong beer

2. Oh a man must be mad or want money bad
   To venture catchin' whales
   For we may be drowned when the fish turns around
   Or our head be smashed by his tail
   Though the work seems grand to the young green hand
   And his heart is high when he goes
   In a very short burst he'd as soon hear a curse
   As the cry of there she blows

3. All hands on deck now for God's sake
   Move briskly if you can
   And he stumbles on deck so dizzy and sick
   For his life he don't give a damn
   And high overhead the great flukes spread
   And the mate gives the whale the iron
   And soon the blood in a purple flood
   From the spout-hole comes a-flyin'

4. Well these trials we bear for nigh four year
   'Til the flying jib points for home
   We're supposed for our toil to get a bonus of the oil
   And an equal share of the bone
   But we go to the agent to settle for the trip
   And we've find we've cause to repent
   For we've slaved away four years of our life
   And earned about three pound ten

*From the singing of A.L. Lloyd, Trevor Lucas
and Martyn Wyndham-Read*

WHEN I WAS A FAIR MAID

1. When I was a fair maid
   About seventeen
   I enlisted in the Navy
   For to serve the Queen
   I enlisted in the Navy
   A sailor lad to stand
   For to hear the cannons rattling
   And the music so grand

   AND THE MUSIC SO GRAND
   AND THE MUSIC SO GRAND
   FOR TO HEAR THE CANNONS RATTLING
   AND THE MUSIC SO GRAND (ETC.)

2. Well the officer that enlisted me
   Was a tall and handsome man
   He said you'll make a sailor
   So come along my man
   My waist being tall and slender
   My fingers long and thin
   And the very soon they learned me
   I soon exceeded them

3. Well they sent me to bed
   And they sent me to bunk
   To lie with a sailor
   I never was afraid
   But taking off my blue coat
   Sure it often made me smile
   For to think I was a sailor
   And a maiden all the while

4. Well they sent me up to London
   For to guard the Tower
   And I'm sure I might be there
   'Til my very dying hour
   But a lady fell in love with me
   I told her I was a maid
   Oh she went unto the Captain
   And my secret she betrayed

5. Well the Captain he came up to me
   And he asked if this was so
   Oh I dare not, I dare not
   I dare not say no
   It's a pity we should lose you
   Such a sailor lad you made
   It's a pity we should lose you
   Such a handsome young maid

6. So it's fare thee well Captain
   You've been so kind to me
   And likewise my shipmates
   I'm sorry to part with thee
   But if ever the Navy needs a lad
   A sailor I'll remain
   I'll put out my hat and feathers
   And I'll run the riggin' again

From the singing of Triona Ni Dhomhnaill

WHISKEY JOHNNY

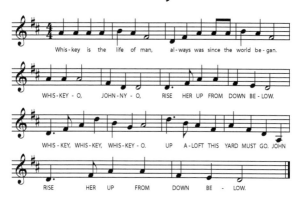

1. Oh whiskey is the life of man
   Always was since the world began

   WHISKEY-O, JOHNNY-O
   RISE HER UP FROM DOWN BELOW
   WHISKEY, WHISKEY, WHISKEY-O
   UP ALOFT THIS YARD MUST GO
   JOHN RISE HER UP FROM DOWN BELOW

2. Oh whiskey is the life of man
   Whiskey from an old tin can

3. Whiskey made my pawn me clothes
   Whiskey gave me a broken nose

4. I thought I heard the old man say
   I treat me crew in a decent way

5. I treat me crew in a decent way
   I gives them whiskey twice a day

6. A glass of whiskey all around
   And a bottle full for the shantyman

WHUP JAMBOREE

WHUP JAMBOREE, WHUP JAMBOREE
OH A LONG-TAIL SAILORMAN COMING UP BEHIND
WHUP JAMBOREE, WHUP JAMBOREE
COME AND GET YOUR OATS ME SON

1. Now the pilot he looked out ahead
   A hand's on the chains and the heaving of the lead
   And the old man roared to wake the dead
   Come and get your oats me son

2. On now we see the Lizard light
   Soon me boys will heave in sight
   Soon be abreast of the Isle of Wight
   Come and get your oats me son

3. Now when we get to the Blackwall Docks
   Those pretty young girls come out in flocks
   With short-legged drawers and their longtail frocks
   Come and get your oats me son

4. Now then we'll walk down Limehouse way
   And all the girls will spend our pay
   We'll not sign on 'til another day
   Come and get your oats me son

From the singing of David Jones, Peter Marston and
Charles O'Hegarty (The Starboard List)

THE WILD GOOSE

1. Did you ever see a wild goose
   Sailin' o'er the ocean
   RANZO, RANZO, WAY-HEY
   They're just like them pretty girls
   When they gets the notion
   RANZO, RANZO, WAY-HEY

2. The other morning
   I was walkin' by the river
   When I saw a young girl walkin'
   With her topsails all a-quiver

3. I said pretty fair maid
   And how are you this morning
   She said none the better
   For the seeing of you

From the singing of Louis Killen

YARMOUTH TOWN

1. In Yarmouth Town there lived a man
   He kept a little tavern down by the strand
   This landlord had a daughter fair
   A pretty little thing with the golden hair

   OH WON'T YOU COME DOWN
   WON'T YOU COME DOWN
   WON'T YOU COME DOWN
   TO YARMOUTH TOWN

2. At night there came a sailor man
   He asked the daughter for her hand
   Why should I marry you she said
   I get all I want without being wed

3. But if with me you do want to linger
   I'll tie a piece of string all around me finger
   As you pass by just pull on the string
   And I'll come down and I'll let you in

4. At closing time the sailorman
   He's gone to the tavern by the strand
   And when he passed by well he pulled on the string
   And she's come down and she let him in

5. Well he's never seen such a sight before
   'Cause the string around the finger was all she wore
   And when he went in and he pulled on the string
   She pulled back the blanket and let Jack in

6. Well the news it soon got around
   And the very next night in Yarmouth Town
   There was fifteen sailors pulling on the string
   And she come down and she let them all in

7. So all young men that to Yarmouth go
   To see the pretty girl with her hair hanging low
   Well all you got do is pull on the string
   And she'll come down and she'll let you in

From the singing of Andy Irvine

YE MARINERS ALL

1. Ye mariners all as you pass by
   Call in and drink if you are dry
   Come spend me lads your money brisk
   And pop your nose in a jug of this

2. Oh mariners all if you've half a crown
   You're welcome all for to sit down
   Come spend me lads your money brisk
   And pop your nose in a jug of this

3. Oh you tipplers all as you pass by
   Come in and drink if you are dry
   Call in and drink think not amiss
   And pop your nose in a jug of this

4. Oh now I'm old and can scarcely crawl
   I've a long grey beard and a head that's bald
   Crown my desire, fulfill my bliss
   A pretty girl and a jug of this

5. Oh when I'm in me grave and dead
   And all my sorrows are past and fled
   Transform me then into a fish
   And let me swim in a jug of this

From the singing of the Dave Swarbrick
(Fairport Convention)

YELLOW GALS

1. Oh once I had a doudou fair
   Come from Mobile Bay

   HURRAH, ME YELLOW GALS, DOODLE LET ME GO
   DOODLE LET ME GO ME GIRLS, DOODLE LET ME GO
   HURRAH, ME YELLOW GALS, DOODLE LET ME GO

2. I picked her up I took her out
   I walked her 'round the town

3. She danced her feet, she swung her hips
   She winked her sassy eye

4. I took her in, I gave her gin
   I laid her on the floor

5. It's all around the town me boys
   Wasn't it a show

6. The mate was drunk, the crew was drunk
   The old man had a load

7. Oh once I had a doudou fair
   Come from Callao

RECOMMENDED READING

Songs of American Sailormen
Joanna C. Colcord
W.W. Norton and Company, Inc., New York, 1938

Shanties from the Seven Seas
Stan Hugill
Routledge & Kegan Paul, London, 1984

Songs of the Sea
Stan Hugill
McGraw-Hill Book Co., New York, 1977

The Oxford Book of Sea Songs
Roy Palmer
Oxford University Press, Oxford, 1986

The Shanty Book, Part I
Richard Runciman Terry
J. Curwen & Sons Ltd., London, 1921

The Shanty Book, Part II
Richard Runciman Terry
J. Curwen & Sons Ltd., London, 1926

Ships, Sea Songs and Shanties
W.B. Whall
James Brown & Son, Glasgow, 1913

COMPILED BY

Sailor, singer and concertina player, Gary Coover has loved sea songs and shanties for many many years. He plays English concertina, Anglo concertina and melodeon, and has written several music books for the Anglo concertina.

For over 15 years he was the host and producer of the "Shepherd's Hey" radio program of British Isles folk music in Houston, Texas. Gary was also a founding member of a traditional British Isles folk band known for their shanties – the "Four Bricks out of Hadrian's Wall".

The band and Gary often volunteered and performed on the 1877 bark *Elissa* in Galveston, Texas, and often joined in on singing sessions both on deck and below.

Gary organized and emceed the dockside music stage for Galveston's "Dickens on the Strand" as well as local concerts by Martin Carthy, Andy Irvine, Louis Killen, John Kirkpatrick, Dave Swarbrick, Cyril Tawney, Tony Rose and many others.

"Four Bricks out of Hadrian's Wall" aboard *Elissa*, c.1983
(Bill Galbraith, Vance Whelply, Kelley Loftus, Gary Coover)

ACKNOWLEDGEMENTS

The songs and shanties in this book are from a variety of sources and wonderful singers, some of whom are no longer with us, having sailed off into the sunset to their next destination. This book is dedicated to their memory and their tireless efforts in keeping these great old songs afloat in our collective memories.

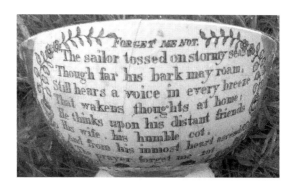

FORGET ME NOT

The sailor tossed on stormy seas
Though far his bark may roam
Still hears a voice in every breeze
That wakens thoughts of home
He thinks upon his distant friends
His wife, his humble cot
And from his inmost heart ascends
The prayer "forget me not"

Printed in Poland
by Amazon Fulfillment
Poland Sp. z o.o., Wrocław